MILLING OPERATIONS
IN THE LATHE

MILLING OPERATIONS IN THE LATHE

Tubal Cain

SPECIAL INTEREST MODEL BOOKS

Special Interest Model Books Ltd
P.O. BOX 327
Poole
Dorset
BH15 2RG

First published by Argus Books Ltd. 1984
Reprinted 1985, 1987, 1989, 1991, 1993, 1995, 1997, 2000

This edition published by Special Interest Model Books Ltd. 2003

Reprinted 2006 (twice), 2008, 2010, 2013, 2017,2020

© Special Interest Model Books Ltd. 2006

ISBN 978-085242-840-5

Printed and bound in Malta by Melita Press

CONTENTS

Chapter 1	Introduction — the Lathe as a Milling Machine	6
Chapter 2	Milling Cutters	12
Chapter 3	Tooth Geometry, Speeds and Feeds and Cutter Holding	23
Chapter 4	Workholding	33
Chapter 5	Milling Attachments	42
Chapter 6	Indexing and Dividing	52
Chapter 7	Procedures and Case Studies	70
Chapter 8	Combined Operations and Complex Milling	88
Chapter 9	Care of cutters	111
Appendices		117
Index		123

CHAPTER 1

Introduction – the Lathe as a Milling Machine

The lathe is by far the most versatile of all machine tools. Though developed as a producer of "solids of revolution", working between centres, the introduction of the headstock – a very long time ago – rendered the production of flat surfaces possible and "surfacing" techniques are mentioned in almost every written record of the lathe. When turning became a leisure occupation – about 400 years ago so far as we know – the wish to apply decoration to plain turned work resulted in the development of a number of auxiliary devices. Some, like the "Rose Engine", were effectively a different machine, and need not concern us. But one device, introduced very early, is what was known as the "drilling instrument".

Fig. 1 shows that fitted to a lathe made by Holtzapffel in 1805. The toolholder is removed and the spindle set in its place. Driven by an "overhead" gear from the treadle and used in conjunction with the dividing circles on the mandrel pulley (this, too, being a very early device) patterns of holes could be produced both

Fig. 1. Drilling spindle of a lathe made in 1805, fluting with a form-drill.

Fig. 2. Ornamental drills, as used in Fig. 1.

on the surface and on the cylinder. The drills could be plain or profiled (some are shown in Fig. 2) and quite elaborate patterns could be produced. The "instrument" could also be used to produce flutes, of plain or complex profile, by traversing the spindle using the feedscrew of the sliderest. In conjunction with the Ornamental Chucks, already highly developed even at that time, quite remarkable work could be done.

Whilst the origin of the Drilling Instrument is unknown, the introduction of what might be termed "revolving tool cutters" is certainly due to Holtzapffel. No doubt he was influenced by the "Wheel Cutting

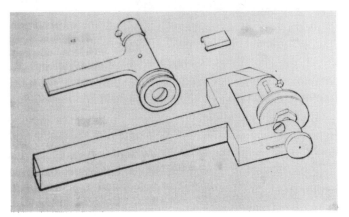

Fig. 3. The "Vertical" cutting frame.

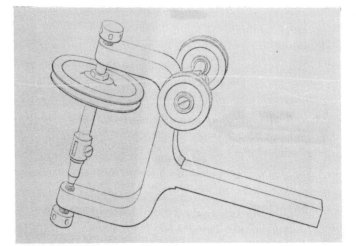

Fig. 4. "Horizontal" cutting frame.

Engines" (which were not lathes) of the clock-maker. The first two to be applied to the lathe were the "Vertical " and the "Horizontal" cutting frames, the adjective in each case referring to the plane of revolution of the cutter, Figs 3 & 4. Again,

the cutter itself could be plain or profiled. We need not concern ourselves with the uses for which they were devised, but it is clear that normal slotting and grooving could be done and that the vertical frame could be and was used as a gear-cutter. These two were followed very quickly by the "Universal" cutting frame, of which Fig. 5 is a relatively modern example (Birch, c.1912). This accepts the same type of tool, but the plane of revolution can be set at any angle, with obvious advantages. (This example is geared, but most were direct driven).

The next development (possibly about 1825?) was perhaps the most ingenious and certainly the most valuable to the ornamental turner, and has its lessons for the model engineer as well. This was the "Eccentric" cutting frame, Fig. 6. It is, in effect, a micrometer adjustable flycutter, and it speaks much for the work of Charles Holtzapffel that it was calibrated on the index to 0.005 inch. Using cutters identical to those for the other cutting

Fig. 5. A geared "Universal" cutting frame, by Birch.

8

Fig. 6. The "Eccentric" cutting frame.

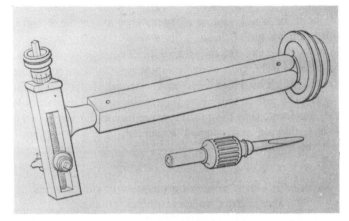

frames (Holtzapffel was a pioneer of such standardisation) its powers were very great indeed. Again, we need not be concerned with "Ornamental " work, but suffice it to say that used in conjunction with the mandrel dividing index it can generate accurate polyhedral solids, and even a perfect hemisphere.

It is interesting to observe that the use of such cutting frames was confined entirely (so far as we can tell) to the amateur ornamental turner. No doubt the needs of the engineering industry of the day were such that there was no call for such devices. However, it is interesting to find that the first application of a rotary tool seems to have been devised for the making of special hexagon nuts – for a model! Fig. 7 shows the arrangement devised in 1829 by James Nasmyth when working with Maudslay on the manufacture of special collar-nuts. These were needed for a model of one of Maudslay's large marine engines. The cutter is described as a "circular file" and was carried in the lathe mandrel, while the circular indexing device was mounted on

Fig. 7. A collar-nut milling machine devised by James Nasmyth, c 1829. The forerunner of the milling machine.

the slide rest. This was so successful that a larger machine was purpose-made for the works, for use on nuts for the full-size engines. Perhaps not the first (and certainly not the last) occasion where the "model engineer" has led the way!

The amateur ornamental turner, and the model engineer if he had such a lathe, now had facilities for producing flat surfaces, cutting slots, gear forming and

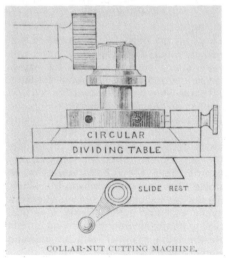

CIRCULAR DIVIDING TABLE

SLIDE REST

COLLAR-NUT CUTTING MACHINE.

9

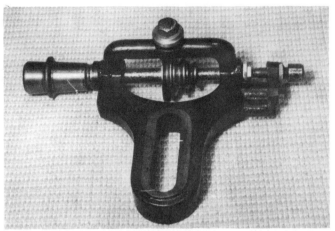

Fig. 8. A Britannia milling spindle of about 1880.

similar, for fluting, and for the generation of accurate prismatic solid shapes. Naturally the ornamental turner was most concerned with "decoration" but as the practice of making engineering models "for fun" developed more and more use was made of these facilities, but adapted to the small engineer's lathe. The cutting frames were made more robust (Fig. 8 is a device by Britannia of 1880) and the "turner" became accustomed to using milling cutters on his lathe. The dividing circles on the headstock pulley were less elaborate but the associated index was made strong enough to meet the higher forces involved in cutting metal. But large flat areas were produced by filing, on hand planing or shaping machines, or on the lathe faceplate. The majority of the milling work done on the lathe used relatively small cutters. In Volume 1 of *Model Engineer*, October 1898, a prize of £2 was awarded to a Mr. R.B.Matthews for an article "The Lathe as a Milling Machine". His devices included the drilling spindle, a robust eccentric cutting frame, a vertical cutting frame, an arbor for carrying cutters on the lathe mandrel, and an indexing workholder.

LIMITATIONS OF THE MACHINE

Writers often refer to the "disadvantages" of the lathe when used as a miller, but true disadvantages are few. The chief is the fact that the lathe lacks one of the essential movements. Work can be traversed across the axis of the mandrel and along it, but not in the vertical plane. This means that an extra vertical slide must be added if full use is to be made of milling processes. The second disadvantage is that except when carrying cutters on an arbor between centres (a relatively rare operation) all work has to be attached to a *vertical surface*, which makes for difficulties in setting. On the other hand, most modern lathes do possess one feature found on few small millers – a considerable speed range. Many model engineers' lathes can be operated at speeds between 25 and 2000 rpm, and almost all can be run at 40 or 50 rpm. This, as we shall see later, is a very important attribute.

The machine has, however,considerable *LIMITATIONS*. The first and most serious is lack of RIGIDITY. All milling involves a continuous sequence of shock loads, and

10

the lathe is not designed to withstand these. Even a small milling machine will have some 20 to 25 sq. ins. of slideway bearing surface, whereas it is a good 3 inch lathe which provides 10 sq.ins. on the saddle, with less on the cross-slide. (And even less still on any vertical slide). The mandrel housing of a miller is very robust compared with that available in a lathe headstock, and there is no comparison between the rigidity of the bed of a lathe compared with a miller of comparable price.

The *power* available at the lathe mandrel is small; it is true that milling machines designed largely for amateur use may have about the same power but this is probably due to "the market" having become accustomed to that limit. But it does mean that many commercial cutters will be far too large for use on the lathe.

The third limitation is the "daylight" available. Using the word "tall" to indicate length along the axis of cutter rotation, the fact that a lathe can accept perhaps 12 inches between work and cutter face is irrelevant; the overhang is too great, whereas with light cuts the same workpiece could comfortably be carried on the horizontal table of a miller. Again, there is but limited space between the top of the cross-slide and the lathe axis — perhaps a couple of inches. A comparable milling machine would accept 6 inches. This situation does limit the work which can be done, especially in facing large castings.

These latter circumstances are, perhaps, not "serious", for much model engineering work will fall within the limit of dimension so imposed. But the limit of power and rigidity does mean that even a half-inch end-mill cannot be used at its full capacity on mild steel or cast iron. The crux of the matter is, then, that rate of metal removal must be adjusted to suit the machine. Provided this is always borne in mind (and assuming that the work can be accommodated in the space) there is little that can be done on a proper milling machine that cannot be done on a lathe; it will just take a little more time, that is all.

CHAPTER 2

Milling Cutters

The action of the tooth of a milling cutter is quite different from that of a lathe tool. Fig. 9 shows that, with the normal rotation relative to the feed, the effective depth of cut is small at the first engagement of the tooth, rising to a maximum at the edge of the workpiece. There will be a sudden release of energy as the chip leaves the parent metal and even if another tooth has started to cut further round the cutter (as it should, if good practice is being followed) there will be a marked "spring back" both of the cutter on its arbor and of the work support. If the rotation is in the opposite direction the shock comes at engagement, but this style of cutting ("down-cut milling") should *never* be used on a lathe, as in the absence of backlash eliminators in the feed-nuts the feed is uncontrollable. In Fig. 10 I show the case of the cutter which has tooth engagement over almost the whole diameter, as might be used in light facing work. Here the depth of cut first increases and then diminishes. There will be much less shock loading, but there is still considerable fluctuation of force liable to cause vibration.

Early types of cutters were designed with a large number of teeth – some even like rotary files – in the hope that this would lessen the problem. In this they were effective, but only at the expense of surface finish and accuracy. Finish suffered because there was not enough space between the teeth to accommodate

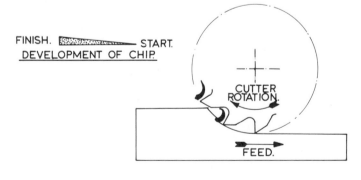

FINISH. ▓▓▓▓▓▓▓▓▓ START.
DEVELOPMENT OF CHIP.

CUTTER ROTATION.

FEED.

Fig. 9. Chip formation when milling. At its thickest part the chip will be about 0.003 inch thick.

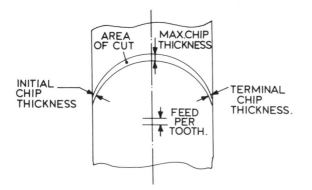

Fig. 10.
Showing the variation in chip thickness when profiling.

AREA OF CUT | MAX.CHIP THICKNESS

INITIAL CHIP THICKNESS

TERMINAL CHIP THICKNESS.

FEED PER TOOTH.

the chips formed during the tooth travel. Accuracy was poor because it was (especially in the early days) difficult to grind every tooth to the same radius of action. Modern cutters have fewer teeth (Fig. 11) and when used properly the tooth spacing will be arranged such that one tooth starts to cut before the previous one has finished. This action is helped by arranging the teeth as a *helix*. Fine pitch cutters may be necessary, however, especially when cutting thin material or taking fine cuts.

TYPES OF CUTTER TOOTH
Teeth may be of two forms. *Fluted Teeth*, Fig. 12, are designed to be sharpened on the top land. The means that the diameter of the cutter is reduced each time it is sharpened. This does not matter on those used for facing, but must be remembered if it is used for cutting a slot, or if dimensional work is being done using feedscrew indexes and allowing for the size of cutter. The clearance angle of the tooth is maintained by setting over the grinding wheel. *Relieved Teeth*, Fig. 13, are used when the profile of the cut must be maintained, as on a gear-cutter or form tool. In this case the tooth is sharpened by grinding the flat front face ONLY, the tooth profile having been maintained all the way down the "relief". These cutters are rather expensive, as a special form relieving machine is needed for their manufacture. The "angle of relief" provides a constant

Fig. 11. Fine and coarse pitch tooth cutters.

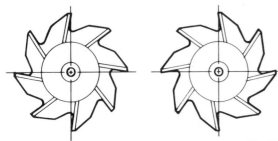

Fig. 12. "Fluted" or "Gashed" tooth cutter.

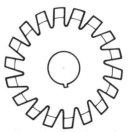

Fig. 13. "Form Relieved" teeth, which have the same profile throughout.

clearance angle throughout.

It should be noted that many fluted tooth cutters *are* used for accurate dimensional profiling – the slot drill is a case in point. Fortunately the model engineer does not subject his cutters to the amount of wear found in industry and it will often suffice simply to grind the end face of the cutter, as it is the sharp corner which suffers most. However, when such cutters are used it is only prudent to remember the sharpening problem, and to set up cutting conditions which will minimise wear. In which connection it should be noted that this does NOT mean reducing the cut to a "shave"; this will be dealt with later, but it can be said now that milling cutters must CUT, and cuts of "the odd thou" *are just those most likely to take the edge off.*

Left, Fig. 15.Side & Face Cutter.
Below, Fig. 14. Slabbing Cutter.
(Photos Clarkson International)

TYPES OF CUTTER

1. *The Slabbing Cutter.* Fig. 14. This is illustrated for completeness, as no lathe likely to be used by a model engineer will have sufficient power available to drive it, nor be rigid enough to carry it. As its name implies, it is used to face slabs or large surfaces. It is often misnamed as a "Roller Mill" – quite a different tool, used for reducing billets to bars in a steelworks by rolling!

2. *The Side-and-Face Cutter.* Fig. 15. This has teeth on the sides or faces as well as on the cylinder, and when used on an arbor between centres can machine the vertical surface of the work. It can be used for cutting slots but, of course, once the face teeth had been ground would not be dimensionally accurate as to width. A variant is the *Slotting Cutter,* Fig. 16. This has teeth on the circumference only – it is really a narrow slabbing cutter. Resharpening does not reduce the width.

3. *Slitting Saw.* Fig. 17. These are relatively thin variants of Fig. 15 and 16; some have teeth on the sides, some not, but the term "saw" is usually applied only to those without. Primarily intended as cutting-off tools they can be used to form narrow slots. Thicknesses vary from as low as 0.004 inch up to 1/4 inch, but it is doubtful whether a 3 inch lathe could cope with much above 1/8 inch. Selection of tooth pitch is important; there should never be less than three teeth in contact,

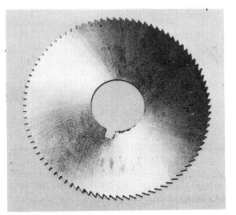

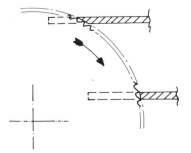

but on the other hand, with thick work the pitch must be large enough to provide adequate chip clearance. If necessary the work may have to disposed with the cutter almost tangentially (Fig. 18) to ensure adequate tooth contact.

4. *Angle-cutters*, Fig. 19. These, as their name implies, are cutters for forming vee-grooves or bevels. They may be single or double angle, and in the latter case the two angles can be different if need be. Special cutters of this type can be had for fluting the teeth of home-made milling cutters and, with a radius at the point, for fluting taps and reamers.

5. *Formcutters*. Fig. 20. As already explained, these must always be of the

Top left, Fig. 16. Slotting Cutter, with no teeth on the sides. Top, Fig. 17, Slitting Saw. Above, Fig. 18. How more teeth can be brought into contact when using a coarse-pitch saw. Bottom left, Fig. 19. Angle Cutter. Below, Fig. 20. Form relieved gear cutter.

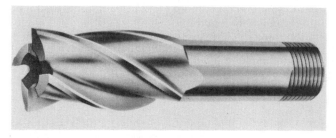

Fig. 21. Endmill (Photo Clarkson International)

form-relieved type. That shown is a gear-cutter, but the profile can be of any reasonable shape. Accurate setting-up of both work and cutter is important as even slight deviations can distort the shape (Though at times advantage may be taken of this fact, to produce a non-standard form. A semi-circular form cutter could, for example, be offset to cut the gullet-shape of a cutter tooth).

6. *The End-mill.* All the cutters so far mentioned are designed to be mounted on an arbor – either between centres or held in a chuck. The end-mill, Fig. 21, is always held in a chuck. That shown has a screwed shank for use in a special collet-chuck (by far the most accurate and safest

Fig. 22. Design (maximum) cutting conditions for an endmill.

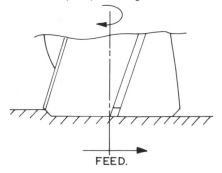

way) but they can be had with plain shanks. They have teeth on the cylinder and on the end, the former usually (and preferably) helical in form. Though often used as facing cutters their prime function is *profiling*, the design cutting condition being shown in Fig. 22, with the maximum depth of cut equal to the cutter diameter and maximum width one quarter of the diameter. They are somewhat unhappy cutting a width more than half

Left, Fig. 23. Shell Endmill (Photo Clarkson International)
Below, Fig. 24. It is helpful to bevel the teeth of cutters used purely for facing.

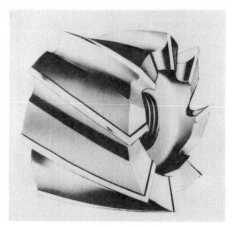

FEED.

the diameter even if the depth is reduced accordingly. Note that if the machine is incapable of accepting the full cut shown in Fig. 22 the *axial* depth of cut should be reduced, not the width, for it is important that at least two teeth should be engaged. THEY ARE *NOT* INTENDED FOR CUTTING SLOTS and will not cut to dimension if so used. If a slot MUST be cut with an end-mill then it should be of a diameter less than the width of the slot and a cut taken down each side separately – with the work-traverse opposing the rotation of the teeth, of course.

7. *Shell End-mills.* Fig. 23. Large (relatively) diameter end-mills on a solid shank would be expensive, and the shell end-mill is an alternative. It is normally held on a short arbor, and retained with an allen screw and thick washer. The drive is normally taken through a cross-key engaging in a slot in the back face, but for model engineers' work the friction drive is often sufficient. If need be a small peg can be fitted on the collar of the arbor to take the drive. Some may be threaded for use on a screwed holder. Though they are, precisely, end-mills and intended for use as in Fig. 22, their larger diameter makes them very handy for facing work. However, if they (or, indeed, any end-mill) are to be used exclusively for facing it is worth while to chamfer the tooth corner as shown in Fig. 24. This corner suffers rapid wear and spoils the cutting action, especially on light finishing cuts, and a chamfer will make a considerable improvement. However, it is fairly important to ensure that each tooth is equal, and if a cutter-grinder is not available it is best merely to stone a very small bevel on each tooth. A suitable arbor for such cutters is shown on page 30.

8. *The "Rippa" cutter.* Fig. 25. This is, in effect, an end-mill with chip-breakers on the teeth. The ordinary cutter produces a

Fig. 25. The Clarkson "RIPPA" type endmill (Photo Clarkson International).

chip which is long in relation to its thickness, and this can lead to difficulties – and also limits the depth of cut. The "Rippa" is formed to make a series of overlapping grooves, each having a discrete chip. The rate of metal removal can be much greater – in sizes below about 1 inch diameter the total area of cut can be as much as four times that of a standard end-mill, though the feed-rate must be reduced somewhat. Provided sufficient power is available at the mandrel the cutter can shift metal at about twice the rate. The finish is surprisingly good on the vertical surface as the multiple "teeth" are arranged in a helix, and is equal to that of an end-mill on the face.

End-mills. shell and solid, and Rippa cutters can be used as small slabbing cutters, but care must be taken, first not to overload them and second, not to reduce the load by reducing the depth of cut. 0.003 to 0.005 inch should be the minimum. Judgement must be used; the cutter is projecting as a cantilever and the

Fig. 26. Comparison between "Standard" and "Long" endmills.

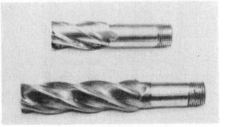

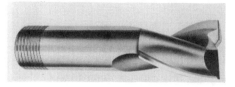

Fig. 27. The Slot Drill; note the unequal length of face teeth. (Photo Clarkson International)

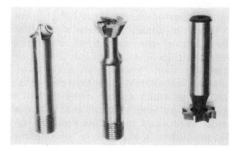

Fig. 28. Left to Right: Corner-rounding, Dovetail, and Woodruffe keyway cutters.

cutting forces can be high – very high if the cutter is not really sharp. "Long Series" cutters (Fig. 26) are available, but these are not really intended for use as wide slabbing cutters but rather to reach down below the top of a tall workpiece.

9. *The Slot-drill.* Though having the appearance of an end-mill this cutter is quite different. First it has two (sometimes three) teeth (Fig. 27) instead of the usual

four or more. Second, on the end face one tooth extends across the centreline. This means that the cutter can be plunged down straight into a face, which cannot be done with an end-mill. If the cutter is sharpened only on this end face it will cut true to dimension, provided the chuck holding it runs true. The finish on the sides of the slot is far better than can be had from a multi-tooth end-mill. They can be used for facing, but not for profiling. The correct (maximum) cut is of a depth equal to half the cutter diameter though this must, of course, be reduced to suit the power available and the rigidity of both cutter – and work-holder.

10. *Tee-slot and Dovetail Cutters.* Fig. 28. These serve the purposes which their names imply. In both cases it is necessary to rough out a plain slot first. In the case of the tee-slot cutter the "size" is sometimes quoted as the size of the bolt for which the slot is needed. One side of the slot is cut at once – they are not slot-drills. The cutters have many applications and inverted dovetail, or "bevelling" cutters are available. Fig. 28 also shows a Corner Rounding cutter.

11. *Woodruffe Keyway Cutter.* Fig. 28. This is similar in shape to the tee-slot cutter. Its diameter and width corresponds to the British Standard or Metric Woodruffe key. It has teeth on the

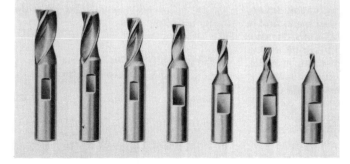

Fig. 29. A set of Clarkson FC3 "Throwaway" cutters; also available with ball ends. (Photo Clarkson International)

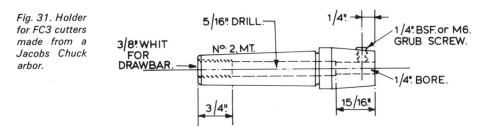

Fig. 31. Holder for FC3 cutters made from a Jacobs Chuck arbor.

5/16" DRILL.

1/4"

1/4" BSF. or M6. GRUB SCREW.

3/8" WHIT FOR DRAWBAR.

N⁰. 2, M.T.

1/4" BORE.

3/4"

15/16"

circumference only. Model engineers seldom need this type of key, but the cutter can be used for slotting connecting rods and for ordinary keyways. The neck is conveniently reduced in diameter adjacent to the head, to clear the shaft being cut.

12. *Ball-ended slot drills.* These have two teeth as a rule, the end being ground to a radius equal to half the cutter diameter. Their main application is the cutting of grooves and flutes, though when set at an angle to the radius of the work they can be used for gulleting. Being slot drills they can be used in a plunging cut to form the seat for a ball-joint. Care must be taken in regrinding, as otherwise the true spherical form will be lost.

13. *"Throwaway" cutters.* Fig. 29. This is a fairly recent introduction, being so cheap (relatively) that in industry they are not worth the time needed to sharpen them. They are three-fluted slot drills which can, within the limitation of length, be used as end-mills. The cutters are surface treated after hardening and cut remarkably freely. The maximum diameter available is 0.250 inch and sizes down to 1/16 inch dia can be had on ¼-inch shank. Standard and "long series" (Fig. 30) are available, as are

Fig. 30. "Long" type FC3 cutter (Photo Clarkson International).

ball ended cutters. All have the same diameter of shank and they are usually held in a Morse taper adaptor, as seen in Fig. 31. This type of cutter is ideal for such work as port-milling and the like.

SINGLE POINT CUTTERS. The cutters so far illustrated are commercial types (though they can be home-made in some cases) and are more or less costly. The single-point milling cutter, often called a FLY-CUTTER, is, for many jobs, an adequate substitute provided its limitations are realised, and can very quickly be made in the workshop. That shown in Fig. 32, for example, is no more than a piece of ¼-inch diameter silver steel bent to shape and hardened at the tip. They are particularly applicable to facing work in brass and light alloy, where the cutting speed can be high enough to avoid the need for a low feed-rate.

This is the first limitation. Suppose we have a fly-cutter to sweep 2 inch diameter. For carbon steel on cast iron a safe cutting speed is about 25ft/min. The mandrel speed will then be about 48 rpm. Even at a feed rate of 0.010 in/rev – which would leave a tolerable, but not a good, finish – the feed-rate can be no more than about ½-inch/minute which with the normal cross-slide feedscrew, means a "handle rate" of 5 rpm; not too easy to keep steady. We shall have more to say about the relative merits of fly-cutters and facing cutters or end-mills for facing large areas later.

Fig. 32. Facing a gunmetal cylinder with a simple but effective flycutter.

The second difficulty arises from the design of the lathe itself. All lathes are (or should be) designed to machine a workpiece very slightly concave when carried on the faceplate. This means that the cross-slide is not EXACTLY at right-angles to the mandrel axis. This is very slight – perhaps 0.002 to 0.003 in./foot when the tolerance on headstock alignment is allowed for. But it does mean that the tool point will cut on the upwards return stroke at the back of the workpiece. This will not matter if the travel of the cross-slide is sufficient to permit the work to run right past the sweep of the cutter, but as fly-cutting is usually resorted to

Fig. 33. A boring head used as a flycutter. Note the white-painted backplate behind.

when the work is too large in area to permit this there will be a discontinuity of cut part way across the surface. The difficulty can at first sight be overcome by reversing the normal traverse direction – i.e. bringing the cross-slide forward so that the tool cuts on the backstroke. This is well enough for light work, but the golden rule when milling should be to ensure that cutting forces are downwards onto the flat shears of the bed. In any case, if the work is too long to clear the cutter completely this will not serve.

The first difficulty can be mitigated by using high-speed steel (or even carbide) but this cannot be manipulated in the form shown in Fig. 32. However, Fig. 33 shows an ordinary BORING HEAD (the photo shows the "A.B.C.") set up as a facing cutter. The tool is a 3/8 dia HSS tool-bit and the radius can be adjusted both by setting over the tool at an angle and by using the micrometer setting slide. This arrangement can be used for "milling" large diameter circular facings, by adjusting the micrometer after each 2 or 3 revolutions; tedious, perhaps, but effective.

Fig. 34 shows another alternative. Here a normal (though rather large section!) boring bar is held in the 4-jaw chuck to provide a flycutter of very large sweep. It might be thought that the ordinary "bent" boring tool could be used, but unfortunately the cutting edge faces the wrong way. It is NOT advisable to reverse the rotation of the lathe to meet this, as the interrupted cut could cause the chuck to unscrew from the mandrel nose. Frankly, I hesitated before using a fly-cutter of such large sweep, but on one occasion when I needed one I applied the device similar to that shown in Fig. 35. Here a bolt has been drilled to accept a 3/16 inch dia HSS toolbit and this can be secured at any desired radius on the lathe faceplate.

a low figure, as much to achieve a good finish as to avoid wear.

ODD CUTTERS. All model engineers have experienced the situation where the odd job arises and there is no alternative but to make a special tool. Fig. 37 is a small vee-cutter made to cut the vee grooves in a brass slide for an old piece of machinery. The cone was first turned, the material being silver steel, and then three flutes milled out with a slot-drill fed endways.

Fig. 34. A large radius flycutter, based on a heavy boring bar.

Fig. 35. (right) Flycutter mounted on faceplate. (Photo Derek Beck)

Fig. 36. Form-flycutter.

FORM FLYCUTTING. Shaped flycutters are, of course, in common use as gear-cutters for small pitch clock gears, but this is not the only application. Fig. 36 shows the profile of a flat cutter made to decorate the entablature of a model beam engine. It is carried in a cutting frame shown in Fig. 5 page 8. It cannot, of course, be reground except on the top flat face, but as it was needed only to machine about half a dozen 6-inch lengths of brass this did not arise. Naturally, the work was roughed out to a more or less triangular shape first, and the feed-rate was kept to

The profiles were backed off slightly with a fine file (Fig. 38) and the piece then hardened and tempered. It may be noticed

Fig. 37. Home-made vee-forming cutter.

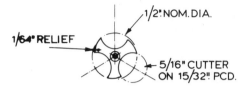

1/64" RELIEF

1/2" NOM. DIA.

5/16" CUTTER ON 15/32" PCD.

Fig. 38. Backing-off the vee-form cutter.

that the three teeth are not of uniform thickness. but this is not important – it just was not worth while setting up an indexing device for a "one-off" job.

Fig. 39 is a fly-cutter rigged up to a machine a semicircular slot of 1 inch radius and about 1 inch long. At the time I had no boring head (the obvious tool to use) and the casting prevented the use of the normal between-centres arbor carrying a side-and-face cutter. The toolbit is, in fact, made from the shank of a broken HSS end-mill. Finally, Fig. 40 shows a very quickly made slot miller, using the shank of a broken drill – fortuitously available in the correct and unusual size. The end was first ground flat and then both backed off and the centre slightly hollow ground. Very crude but despite the received opinion that the shanks of drills are relatively soft the cutter performed its office perfectly, though I doubt if its life would be very long if used frequently.

The actual manufacture of special cutters would need a book to itself, but fortunately when such are needed the

Fig. 39. Radial flycutter – almost a boring tool!

writers of articles in model magazines usually give full instructions. A few notes on clearances and the like are given in the next chapter and if these are followed little difficulty should be experienced in devising the odd "one off" needed now and then. The hardening and tempering of the cutter also needs a book* and in this connection I would suggest that thought be given to the use of casehardened teeth. There is really no need for solid tool-steel when a tool is to be used only the once and casehardened teeth will actually be somewhat harder than tool-steel which has been tempered (and certainly harder than HSS). This is a point often over-

Fig. 40. An endmill made from a broken drill.

looked. A properly hardened carbon steel tool is actually HARDER than a high-speed steel equivalent, and will remain so provided that it is not allowed to get hot. Carbon steel also gives a somewhat better finish if the edge is properly honed. The ONLY virtue of HSS is that it can cut much faster – perhaps twice as fast. But if it can be kept cool, both by using a low cutting speed and, where appropriate, a water-soluble oil cutting fluid, the carbon steel tool will take as deep a cut and last longer. A casehardened tool is harder still, as of course, it does not need tempering. A few notes on this and other aspects of home-made cutters are included in Chapter 9.

* (see Hardening, Tempering and Heat Treatment, No. 1 in the Argus Workshop Practice series).

CHAPTER 3

Tooth Geometry, Speeds & Feeds and Cutter Holding

The majority of model engineers using the lathe for milling will accept the tooth angles found on the cutter "as bought", and as most which are stocked by tool dealers will be "general purpose" cutters there is little need to worry about them – though some care may have to be exercised when dealing with "surplus" tools, some of which may be specials, However, some knowledge of the necessary rakes and clearances is of value, both in diagnosing faults if anything goes wrong and when making cutters. Those who own a cutter-grinder will usually find setting details for the various types of tooth in the handbook.

Fig. 41 shows the nomenclature used – the rakes etc have been somewhat exaggerated for clarity. It will be realised that a straight flute cutter with side teeth (such as an endmill or a side-and-face cutter) can have no axial rake, but a helical flute cutter cannot avoid rake. In cases where the helix angle is such that the rake is excessive it is necessary to stone the edge of each tooth to reduce it – just as we do to a drill when taking heavy cuts in brass. Those who read the engineering press, or who fall into conversation with production engineers, may be forgiven if they wonder about the merits of "negative rake" (Fig. 42). As such it has little virtue; its merit is that the cutting angle, shown in Fig. 42, is increased and the tooth point is stronger. It is almost imperative when cutting hard materials with tungsten

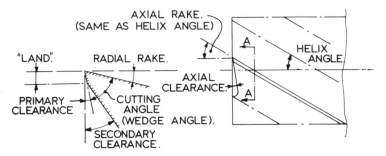

Fig. 41. Cutter Nomenclature.

23

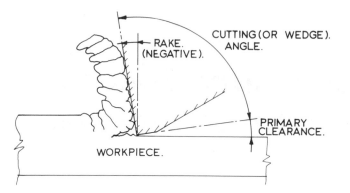

RAKE. (NEGATIVE).

CUTTING (OR WEDGE). ANGLE.

Fig. 42. Action of a "Negative Rake" cutter.

PRIMARY CLEARANCE.

WORKPIECE.

carbide tools, as the tool material is very brittle, but not elsewhere. The power consumption goes up markedly, so that there is no point in even trying negative rake on a milling cutter used in the lathe!

The clearance angle is important. It will be appreciated that the action of a milling tooth is similar to that of a boring tool, except that the cut is entirely on the cylindrical face and not on the side. This means that the smaller the cutter the more important the peripheral clearance becomes. True, small cutters have smaller lands on the teeth, but equally, the amount of wear needed to eliminate the clearance is small also. When making flycutters and especially flat form cutters it is very important to keep this in mind.

The "blunting" of endmills and side-and-face cutters is always characterised by complete loss of clearance on the corner of the tooth, causing rubbing and overheating at this vulnerable point. Reference has already been made to the desirability of stoning a small chamfer, or even a radius, at this corner when the tool is used for facing duties. The chamfer or radius will automatically acquire a cutting rake, but the need for clearance must not be forgotten.

At first sight it might be assumed that the teeth on the end of an endmill will not

cut at all, if all the metal removal is done by the teeth on the cylinder, and the same would appear to apply to slot drills except when plunging, and to side-and-face cutters. This is true to some extent, but these end or facing teeth do have the job of removing the machining marks which would otherwise appear. If blunt they will trap tiny pieces of swarf and do more harm than good, the swarf cutting circular tears on the machined face. This being so the end teeth are often retouched with an oilstone; when this is done care must be taken to preserve the correct clearance — or at least, as near as possible.

Recommended angles can be found in the table opposite. There is quite a range for each material; the "middle of the range" will serve for most purposes. In general power will be saved if the larger rakes are used on materials which would produce a curly chip when machining, but for "grabby" metals like brass the less rake the better as the milling process tends to "drag up" the clearance in slide feedscrew nuts. For really tough material the minimum of both rake and clearance should be used. Slitting saws have zero rake as a rule.

The axial rake is, of course, preset by the helix angle on helical tooth cutters — it can be reduced by stoning or grinding, but

24

Material	Radial Rake degrees	Axial Rake degrees	Clearance degrees (see note)
Cast Iron (Grey)	5–10	5–10	4–7
Cast Iron (Hard)	3–5	3–5	4–7
F.C. Mild Steel	8–12	8–12	3–5
B.D. Mild Steel	6–12	6–12	3–5
Stainless Steel	3–8	3–5	3–5
Al. Alloy	10–15	10–15	10–12
Brass, 60/40	3–5	3–5	10–12
Brass, hard	0–5	0–5	10–12
Copper	10–15	8–12	10–12
P.Bronze	3–6	0–4	4–7

Note. 1. For general purposes, clearance angles should range from 4–5° for cutters $2\frac{1}{2}$ in. dia to 13° for 1/8 in dia.

2.The tabled clearances should be applied only to a "land" about 1/64–1/32 in. wide; behind this a further clearance of about 5° more should be ground.

cannot be increased. On the other hand, axial rake on straight-flute cutters is fixed at zero.

To conclude this section, an important point must be emphasised. Owing to the peculiar action of the cutter the *rate of feed* will reduce the effective clearance angle when facing, or when cutting slots with a slot-drill. If the "land" is wide and the clearance angle small actual interference can result. THIS IS THE MOST COMMON CAUSE OF BREAKAGE OF SMALL ENDMILLS AND SLOT DRILLS, and cutters which appear to be blunt may well be suffering from overdriving.

CUTTING SPEEDS AND FEEDS. Two factors are involved. First, the power available to "shift metal", and, second, the acceptable rate of wear of cutting edge. In both cases the data published in "Production Engineering" tables and "Engineering Yearbooks" can be misleading to the model engineer. On the first point, any milling machine with 3 HP available would be regarded as "tiny" in a production workshop. We have, as a rule, about half a horsepower available and a lot of

that is lost in the belt drive. Our machine is far less rigid, too. The best we can hope for is the removal of perhaps one quarter to one third of a cubic inch of steel or cast iron per minute on a $3\frac{1}{2}$inch lathe. The amount we can remove when TURNING is not relevant – milling is a different kettle of fish.

On the second point, cutting speeds in industry are geared to an economic overall cost of production. It pays to drive cutters hard and to regrind often. Few model engineers have cutter-grinders, and we must treat our tools accordingly, AND bear in mind that we are using a lathe and not a milling machine. A blunt turning tool can soon be remedied, but an endmill cannot.

CUTTING SPEED. For HSS endmills the following cutting speeds can be used as a basis, but see also the note at the end of "Feed Rate" Section.

Cast Steel, Malleable Iron, Monel, Stainless steel	35ft/min.
Cast Iron, Bronze, Drawn MS, Gunmetal	60ft/min.
Brass, Free-cutting MS, Muntz Metal	100ft/min.

Al.Alloy, Tufnol,
"screw-brass". 200-300 ft/min.
Slot-drills can be run perhaps 10% faster. *Side-and-face cutters* can be run at the above speeds if the mandrel or arbor is stiff enough to avoid chatter. Single point flycutters can be treated as boring tools, but again the stiffness of the tool (and work) must be taken into account. Subject to what follows the rule should be to reduce speed if in any doubt.

Finishing cuts. For small cutters, 1/8in. diameter and below, the above speeds when translated into RPM may well be beyond the capacity of the machine – you must then run as fast as possible. Cutting speed may be found by writing

$$RPM = \frac{(3.8 \times Ft/min)}{Cutter\ dia\ in\ inches}$$

FEED RATE. Milling practice is to use a figure known as "Tooth Load". This is the feed per revolution *per tooth,* so that the feed in ins/min is the product of speed in RPM, number of teeth, and tooth load. Tooth load varies very little from one material to another, but it does go down rapidly as the cutters get smaller. (We are not, of course, concerned with "Industrial" cutters, which can be 6 inches to a foot or more in diameter!) The chart, Fig. 43, plots a "Tooth load Factor" against cutter diameter for those between 1/16 inch and 1 inch diameter. This is for HSS endmills working at the depth of cut shown in Fig. 22. For slot-drills – again working full depth – the factor may be increased by 50% (but remember that they have only two teeth). When used on a very light cut, as for surfacing, the rates may be doubled, provided that this gives an acceptable finish.

The factor "F" is practically constant for all materials in the sizes we normally use – the actual feed rate will depend on

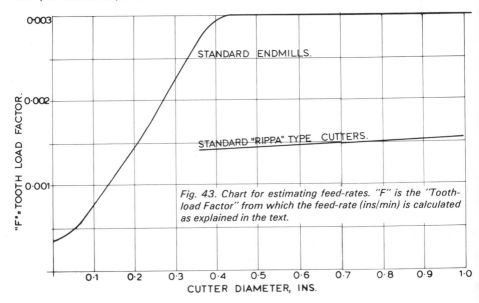

Fig. 43. Chart for estimating feed-rates. "F" is the "Tooth-load Factor" from which the feed-rate (ins/min) is calculated as explained in the text.

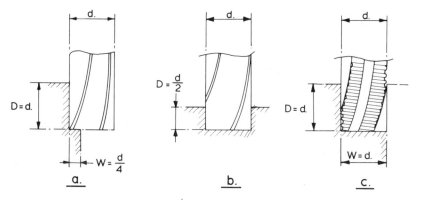

Fig. 44. Maximum depths of cut for various types of cutter.

the number of flutes and the RPM, as well as "F".

Feed Rate = "F" × Cutter Dia(Ins) × RPM × No. of Flutes. = (inches/minute) The feed rate thus depends on the CUTTING SPEED, and this varies according to material being cut, as mentioned above. It is always tempting to reduce the feed rate if the cutter exhibits distress, but though a *slight* reduction does no harm this is, in general, a mistake. The *depth of cut* should be reduced and the feed rate maintained. With very small cutters the "tooth load" is very small indeed and you will recall from Fig. 9 that the cut seen by the tooth starts at a very low figure. Very slow feed rates cause the tooth to rub at the beginning of the cut, and this causes poor finish.

The comments so far refer to the "normal" situation of the model engineer, who has no facilities for proper cutter grinding, and who is more concerned with tool life than with rate of metal removal. However, if you have a "Quorn" or similar, and care to spend time resharpening every now and then, you can work faster. I show in Appendix I the recommended INDUSTRIAL speeds and feeds, and subject to the rigidity of your setup you can approach these. You will note, however, that the TOOTH LOAD is nearly as above – the difference is in the increased cutting speed.

DEPTHS OF CUT. The rule here is simple: the depth of cut should be as large as the available power will permit up to the limit prescribed for the type of cutter. (And, of course, the amount of metal you wish to remove!) To refresh your memory I show in Fig. 44 the design cutting depths for endmills, slot drills, and "Rippa" cutters. These may look formidable to those not accustomed to milling, but it will be realised that the *thickness* of the chip is unaffected by the depth "D" – it depends only on the feed rate. A full depth cut produces a long, but thin, chip. For the average 3 inch lathe in good condition a rough estimate of the size of cut can be made by multiplying feed rate in inches per minute by the depth and width, "D" and "W"; if the proposed cut works out at much above one third of a cubic inch per minute for cast iron or steel you will probably overload the machine. For aluminium alloys and soft brass higher rates may be possible, but the depths and widths of Fig. 44 should still not be exceeded.

27

Model engineers frequently use endmills as facing cutters. This is fair enough for finishing cuts, but end-mills are not happy when taking a deep cut of width approaching the cutter diameter, and downright miserable if asked to cut a slot. The "Rippa"*will* work full width, as will the slot drill. If much metal has to be removed it is best either to rough out with a series of cuts as at 44a and then take a facing cut, or to use one of the other types of cutter and change over for finishing. Shell endmills ARE endmills, and designed for use as Fig. 44a, but again with light cuts can be used almost full width for finishing. The maximum depth of cut for side-and-face cutters or slitting saws is academic so far as work in the lathe is concerned, as there is not enough power to use them to the full.

For flycutters the situation is rather different. They can be treated as ordinary boring tools, but as soon as the depth of cut becomes large the shock load at the beginning or end of contact causes problems. The feed rate can be increased to perhaps 0.005 inch per revolution for most materials. The rule here must be to work at a depth of cut which the machine and work seem to be prepared to accept. Do NOT forget the workholder; the shock load can easily displace a machine vice – it happens even on full-size milling machines occasionally!

To sum up. The cutting speed is the main factor determining tool life. The figures suggested above are not critical, but when in doubt, use a lower speed. Feed rate is governed by the tooth load. Too high a tooth load will result in poor finish and may cause "interference" on the primary clearance. Too low a feed rate will cause rubbing, especially if the cutter is a bit worn. Again, the rates derived from Fig. 43 are not critical. The depth and width of cut which can be used depends more on the rigidity of the machine and the power available than on anything else, and should be as high as can be managed (though preferably not beyond those shown in Fig 44) with comfort. *Very light* cuts should be avoided, especially if the cutter is not dead sharp. In general, if the machine seems to be cutting happily there is no need to worry too much about exact feeds, speeds, and depth of cut!

CUTTER HOLDING. The classic milling arbor, carried between centres, is of limited use when milling in the lathe. First, the clearance between arbor and cross-slide is small and as seen in Fig. 45, will not permit any reasonable size of machine vice to be used. Secondly, the need for clearance between tailstock and saddle means that the arbor will be relatively long and slender. The third difficulty is that due to the direction of rotation of the cutter the work ought to be fed from the back of the lathe to the front. The cutting forces then tend to be upwards, but the saddle is designed to take downward thrust.

Nevertheless, there are situations where such a mandrel is useful, and Fig. 46 shows the arrangement. The cutter (usually of half-inch bore) is held against the shoulder by recessed spacers, and it is important that these be a good fit on the mandrel and be faced square to the bore. A narrow double-ended spacer can be made if it is desired to carry two cutters for straddle milling operations, but in my experience the arbor is used mainly for slitting-saws and, occasionally, for gear-cutters. The usual set-up is with the arbor between centres, but if the driving end is held in a 3- or preferably a 4-jaw chuck this does stiffen up the assembly. The end of the arbor is turned down with a shoulder so that this can be located positively against the chuck jaws. It is not usual to provide a key for the cutter, even though the latter may have a keyway. The depths of cut which the slender arbor permits are unlikely to cause cutter slip, and in a way this can be a safety device if excess load occurs accidentally.

ENDMILLS are usually held in the lathe chuck. The slight runout will not matter unless co-ordinate setting is being used, in which case the cutter should be mounted in the 4-jaw independent chuck and set true. The greater problem with the chuck is wear on the jaws. This means that the cutter shank is unsupported at the outer end, the end which matters. A strip of paper round the shank at the front edge of the jaws will help a great deal – use paper rather than shimstock. However, there is another consideration which makes the use of the independent chuck desirable. The grip must be really tight, if anything other than a slight finishing cut is involved. The vibration can cause the cutter slowly to move in or out of the chuck jaws and if an attempt is made to counteract this with a self-centring chuck the scroll may be overstrained. SLOT DRILLS should always be carried in the 4-

Fig. 45. "Problems with Arbors". This vice will not pass beneath.

jaw chuck and set true if an accurate slot is to be cut. (The usual tolerance on cutters below inch dia is −0.0005 to −0.0013 inch, but an endmill will lie between −0.0005 to +0.0025 inch).

Bar-holding collets do offer an accurate means of securing cutters, but though they may hold the cutter securely in the rotationary mode there is more risk of the cutter moving axially. The collet is hard, as

Fig. 46. Typical design of milling cutter arbor. The smaller end must be long enough to allow the tailstock to clear the lathe saddle.

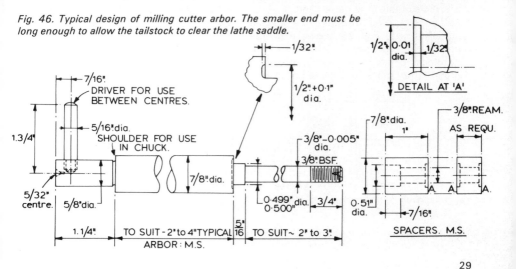

Fig. 47. Small cylindrical and vee cutters mounted on 8mm collet arbors.

is the cutter shank if it is HSS, and this combination is very slippery. A depth stop within the collet will prevent movement inwards, but there is no means of preventing the cutter from "walking outwards". Small cutters mounted on 8mm "collet arbors" (Fig. 47) may, of course, be held in an adaptor held in the taper of a larger lathe if a suitable drawbar is used.

SHELL END MILLS require a special stub-arbor, and Fig. 48 shows a design which can be used either in the "Autolock" chuck mentioned later or in a normal lathe chuck. It will be noted that

there is provision for a drawbar in the latter case. The diameter of the shank is made to suit the largest collet of the smaller "S" type Autolock, but can be larger if for use only in the lathe chuck; the stiffer the assembly the better. The drive to the cutter is taken through the small peg (though friction would probably be adequate) and the adaptor is drawn back until the shoulder butts on the chuck jaws before finally tightening the chuck.

A similar adaptor can be used for gear cutters, side-and-face cutters etc, but the distance between chuck face and cutter may have to be extended to bring the cutter to a reasonable position relative to the cross-slide. This extension should be of the maximum diameter possible; it would be unwise to extend the arbor for more than an inch or so as the overhang would then be excessive.

The majority of the endmills and slot-drills sold today have screwed shanks to fit one or other of the proper milling chucks. Fig. 49 shows the Autolock. This is carried on a taper which fits direct into the milling machine or lathe mandrel. (No. 2 M.T. is usual for lathe work). The taper shank is screwed for a drawbar and this *must* be used. The body carries a collar with a left-hand thread, Fig. 49a. This is the *damping ring* and is intended to be tightened against the mandrel nose once

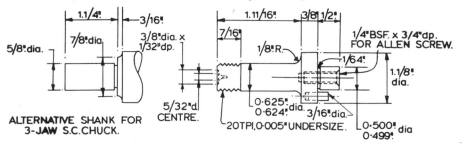

Fig. 48. Arbor for the shell endmill shown in Fig. 23. Right − to fit Clarkson "Autolock" chuck. Left − for use in s/c three-jaw chuck.

Fig. 49a. The Autolock
chuck in section — see
text.

Fig. 49b. Autolock
chuck in service,
showing the "damping
ring" screwed up
against the mandrel
nose. Note also the
white backplate which
both reflects light and
protects the mandrel
nose thread.

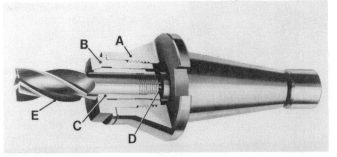

the drawbar is tight. It stiffens the assembly, and is not needed on larger machines with bigger tapers. It is NOT a device for freeing the chuck from the taper, though it can be used as such.

Referring to Fig. 49 the body, A, carries a locking sleeve, B, which, in turn, carries the collet, C. The sleeve with the collet is inserted into the body and screwed up until the shoulder butts. It is then tightened with the special spanner. The cutter, E, is inserted and screwed up hand tight, when the centre in its shank will abut onto the centre at D. In action, if the cutter is not quite tight enough the first touch with the work will take it up further, at the same time automatically tightening the collet on the shank. The cutter cannot move up or down thereafter — indeed, if the cutter is taken out and replaced the projection will be found to be within the odd thou or so of the original position.

Each chuck has four collets in the set and the "small" chuck will accept from 1/16 inch up to 25/32 inch dia. cutters — or the metric equivalents. (Metric holder collets are needed for metric cutters). A large size IS available, but not with a No. 2 M.T. shank; this carries cutters from 13/16 up to 2 inch diameter. A similar type — the "Dedlock" chuck — is available for carrying shell endmills and short overhung slabbing cutters, but this is too large to fit most lathes.

Both types of chuck are relatively costly, though not as expensive as a precision 3-jaw chuck, the alternative commercial product. They may be considered not really worth while unless a great deal of milling is done. However, for the serious practitioner this type of holder (there are others on the market on the same principle) is by far the best. And as many milling machines used by model engineers also have No. 2 M.T. sockets the chuck can be used there also, should the Christmas stocking be found properly filled some time!

Those who have made themselves a master-and-slave chuck system can, of course, make up "slaves" to accept both plain shank and threaded cutters. Fig. 50 shows one such, carrying a FC3 "throwaway" type endmill, though the same slave can accept any 1/4 inch shank cutter. It is only necessary to make a

31

slave, bored when held in the master, to suit the shank diameters of the cutters you have. Fortunately these are more or less standard diameters these days, but a "special" takes very little time to make. I find that I can hold most cutters simply with a set- or grub-screw, but you can easily grind a flat if you like. For endmills and slot-drills up to $\frac{1}{2}$-inch diameter the master-slave system is as accurate a cutter-holder as anything available and, of course, has the added merit that it serves for many other purposes as well. It can hold the centring point in one slave, to be replaced by the cutter slave when ready.

The really important point to watch in holding any type of cutter is axial security – along the axis of rotation of the cutter. On some materials (especially soft brass)

the inevitable rake on a spiral-flute cutter can cause it to "walk into cut", and the vibration found on most milling work can encourage movement. This vibration will rapidly loosen any Morse taper if no drawbar is used. It is a bit disconcerting to find the cut getting deeper and deeper along the feed-line! (yes, it has happened to me,too!) Cutter slip in the rotational sense may not be so serious; to be avoided, of course – it is not the best type of "safety valve" against overloading, as some would have us believe. The second important factor, more important for slot-drills than for endmills, is cutter runout. For normal facing work a GOOD 3-jaw chuck is sufficiently accurate, but for serious slotting it is wise to correct any error if you can.

CHAPTER 4

Workholding

The usual objective of milling is to produce flat surfaces. This means that a number of attributes of the lathe, unimportant when turning, become prime considerations when milling. I have already referred to one – the fact that the lathe is deliberately built to turn concave on the faceplate by a very small amount. This means that a large radius flycutter will "interfere" on the rearward part of its revolution by, perhaps, 0.001 inch or so. There are other reference planes, too, which should be checked.

REFERENCE PLANES. Clearly, work must be set true in the vertical plane, but this normally presents no problem as the lathe-bed can be used as a base. However, there are cases where a square applied to the work cannot sit on the bed. The truth of the top of the cross-slide relative to the bed is only of marginal importance when turning (in fact, it is only of any importance at all when boring on the saddle) so this should be checked crosswise by setting a dial indicator in your scribing block on the bed and traversing the saddle. You will, I think, find perhaps 0.001 inch error over the width. Check that this is not affected by the locking screw – if it is, then your slide gibstrip is probably not tight enough in

normal use. There may be a similar difference between the height of the slide surface above the bed at the BACK of the rear bedway and the FRONT of the front bedway. These errors are within the limits to which you can expect to work, and you can safely square up from the top of the cross-slide. If they are excessive you must seek out the cause and rectify it – unfortunately this book is not the place to deal with machinery renovation, or I could suggest something!

We need also to set work square transversely, across the bed. The concave turning alignment referred to prevents us from using the faceplate (or a chuck face) as a reference plane, though the probable error (better than 0.002 inch per foot) is small. On most machines the concavity is attained by setting over the headstock, so that we can be reasonably sure that the cross-slide *moves* at right angles to the bed. But in squaring up we would normally use the front face of the slide and this need not necessarily be square to the slides. This should be checked; again, if it is within one or two thou.per foot it is as close as can be expected. At the same time check the squareness of the tee-slots to this face, for these also provide a useful reference plane. I have a piece of parallel

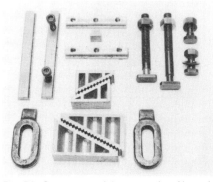

Fig. 51. Some essential accessories. Note the Tee-slot bars and the Picador adjustable packing blocks.

strip which fits the slots closely against which to bed my try-square when necessary.

PACKING, CLAMPS, AND BOLTS. The actual cutting time when milling is a very small proportion of the time taken in setting up the work; I have been at it a long time but even now I still find that the one "gadget" needed is not there. So, a little thought on this aspect may save a lot of time later. Fig. 51 shows a selection of "aids to production". On the right are four classical tee-bolts, which can be made in any length required. A perfectly legitimate descendant of the type used on a milling machine, but guaranteed to reveal the weakness of the lathe. If used on the

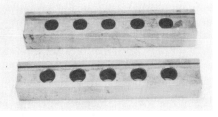

Fig. 52. Steel parallels, "H" shaped, with holes through the web.

cross-slide slots, any reasonable tightness of the nut may cause sufficient distortion of the cross-slide to stiffen up its movement. It may not affect accuracy, but is a nuisance. If pulled up TOO tight there is also a risk of fracturing the edge of the slot. (That is why the two longer bolts, home made, have thin heads, so that they will give way first)

A preferable arrangement is the TEE-BAR, seen at the top and left of the photo. These are machined from rectangular strip to be a reasonable fit to the slots, and then tapped, 1/4 or 5/16 inch BSW or BSF, to fit set-screws or studs. That on the left, carrying two allen screws, is made to fit a machine vice. These bars distribute the load in the slot much better and cause negligible distortion of the slide. The two "dogs" in the lower half of the photo are familiar enough. I have a set, but I must confess that they turn out to be too clumsy more often than not, and my "bit box" is full of odd clamp bars etc. which are often preferable.

In the centre are shown two pairs of packing blocks, obtainable commercially, which I have found to be great time savers. They replace the odd blocks of this and that necessary under clamps etc and being of a relatively soft alloy the risk of burring the surface of the slide is diminished. Fig. 52 shows a pair of PARALLELS. These are used under already machined surfaces of the workpiece to support it at the required height. Most of mine are simple rectangular bar, checked (and occasionally filed or scraped) to be parallel, but this pair is slightly different. They are "I" shaped and have holes through. They are truly parallel both ways, so that they can be laid on their side with a passage through for any securing bolts holding the work above. There is absolutely no need for such to be hardened and ground so long as you take care of them, remove burrs from time to time, and occasionally check that they remain parallel.

VICES. The machine vice is the most convenient workholder, subject to being able to hold the vice itself. We have already seen that the arbor carried between centres may interfere with the vice, but in all other cases there is usually some way of securing it . Fig. 53 shows two vices, the larger one having counterbored holes through the slides to accept the allen screws associated with a pair of tee-slot bars. There is also a recess in the side into which conventional clamps can be fitted. The two tapped holes on top of the jaws are for attaching auxiliary vee jaws.

The smaller vice has a bar secured to each side — a machine screw at each end and a couple of dowels in between to take the shearing load. Two tee-bars like the longer shown in Fig. 51 are set *across* the vice in the slots, and the heads of the screws with hefty washers just engage with these bars. Both of these are sold as good class drilling vices, and very little work was needed on either to ensure that the jaw faces were square, both across the vice and to the base. A little more work was needed on both to ensure that work sitting down on the base was parallel to the surface on which the vice sat, but this was only a case of gentle scraper work. The result is that if the vice is set square there is little doubt about the work being square also. Which leads to an essential, but not illustrated, accessory; the *rawhide mallet*. It is IMPERATIVE that work gripped in the vice should be tapped down into the jaws, as the act of gripping usually displaces it by the odd thou. or so. Packing underneath will usually be found to be loose until this is done. However, some caution must be adopted, as too heavy a blow may move the vice under its clamps.

Fig. 53. 1½ inch and 3 inch machine vices. Note the holding down arrangements.

ANGLEPLATES. This is almost an essential, and more than one may well be needed. In most articles the "open ended" type, machined inside and out, is usually recommended, but I must confess to liking the added stiffness which arises from the end ribs. Machined *ends* are, however, essential if the angleplate is to be used for marking out. Fig. 54 shows a typical application, where a steel sub-base has been bolted to the angleplate to carry the work. The ADJUSTABLE ANGLEPLATE, Fig. 55, has many applications, but in the "obvious" setup there is a limit to the thickness of the work which can be carried, as it may come above the centreline of the cutter.

Fig. 54. An angle-plate in service with an auxiliary workholding plate.

35

Fig. 55. An adjustable angle-plate (Photo James Neill PLC)

VEE-BLOCKS. These have more uses than the natural one holding circular work, as shown in Fig. 56. Here an engine cylinder, already bored, is carried on a mandrel supported in the vees and clamped down whilst the portface is machined. Almost invisible is the toolmakers's jack (a simple support screw) which obviates any risk of the work rotating on the mandrel. These are toolmakers' vee-blocks, ground on all surfaces,

Fig. 56. Use of vee-blocks and arbor. Note the jacking screw – see text.

and can be relied upon to be "matched", so that they can be used as parallel packing if need be. However, the photo shows one of my mistakes – there should be a piece of paper between the blocks and the top of the cross-slide; desirable at all times, but essential if any accessory is bolted down.

A few examples of what might be called "plain" workholding are seen in the photos. Fig. 57a and b shows the use of two angleplates together to hold a large engine base. This is about as large a piece as can be managed in a 3 inch lathe

Fig. 57a and b. Two dissimilar angle-plates in use to hold large work. The flycutter of Fig. 34 is in use.

without resetting, and even as shown there was slight interference at the end of the cut. Fig. 58 shows two arches simply clamped down to the topslide to machine the ends, both at one setting, whilst Fig. 59 is the facing of a steel block. Fig. 60 shows a machine vice holding a block of cast gunmetal being roughed to square and Fig. 61 one of the few applications of the arbor supported cutter. Here the machine vice is carrying four square bars being faced to equal length.

THE VERTICAL SLIDE. While a great deal of milling can be done using the vice, angleplate and vee-block alone there is no doubt that the absence of movement in the third plane – vertically – is a great hin-

Fig. 60. Use of the vice on an angle-plate; squaring up a GM casting.

Fig. 58. (top) A simple setup for squaring the feet of a pair of arches.
Fig. 59. Facing the edge of a steel plate using simple packing on the cross-slide.

drance. The vertical slide remedies this deficiency and though even the strongest is relatively flimsy it literally "makes all the difference". Fig. 62a and 62b show the two Myford variants. That on the left is the "fixed" slide; movement is possible only in the vertical direction. On the right is the "swivelling" type, which can be tilted over so that the slide movement can be at any

angle to the cross-slide top face. In addition the whole issue can be swivelled round about its base fixing.

The fixed slide is the more rigid, but the swivelling type has a wider table and facilitates setting up. Both will travel to about 1 inch below the top surface of the cross-slide. The fixed slide has a total travel of about 4 inches, that of the swivelling slide being 3 inch. There are

Fig. 61. A side-and-face cutter squaring off the ends of four bars at once.

Fig. 62(a). The Myford Fixed or "plain" vertical slide, set on the MYFORD raising block.
Fig. 62(b). The Myford swivelling vertical slide.

arguments in favour of each and against each. I have found that occasions when the swivelling feature is essential are rare, but when they are needed then the fixed slide is very difficult to use as a substitute, sometimes impossible. On the other hand, the additional travel of the fixed type has more than once saved the day. I managed with just the swivelling slide for some 30 years, but since I bought the fixed one as well I seem to have used it the more often.

Fig. 63 shows the Edgar Westbury vertical slide, which also incorporates a dividing and milling spindle (dealt with later). The castings for this are still marketed by Woking Precision Models Ltd, and there are no difficult machining operations involved in its manufacture. The built-in dividing and milling feature is very useful indeed, and though the unit is

heavy this is no disadvantage when milling; mass is the most effective vibration damper there is!

In setting up all vertical slides it is essential to see that the reference faces are square, and I would advise the checking of any NEW purchase to ensure that the slide itself is square to the base. An error here is very unlikely, though it CAN happen – but do not forget that it will have been made to a tolerance, and better than 0.001 inch per foot is good! The use of a sheet of paper between the slide and the cross-slide of the lathe is advised. This both neutralises the effects of any slight bruises on either (which you really ought to have seen to as soon as they occurred, of course!) *and* gives a better frictional grip. A similar piece of paper between vice and slide is worth while, too.

Examples of machining operations are

38

given later in the book, but Fig. 64 illustrates the advantage of the vertical slide quite clearly. The portface of this cylinder could easily have been machined by using either an angle-plate or by setting it up on the cross-slide, but in both cases either a fly-cutter or a fairly large endmill would have been needed. As it is it can be machined across taking two or three traverses with a small and cheap cutter. Further, at the same setting it will be possible later to mill out the steam ports. The vertical slide does, in effect, *convert* the lathe to a milling machine, albeit with the disadvantage that the work supporting table is vertical instead of horizontal.

BLOCKS OF WOOD. Nobody ever pays any attention to me when I extol the virtues of the "little bit of wood" as a workholding device, but it is one of the most useful expedients when nothing else will serve. The example in Fig. 57, for instance, could have been set up in half the time by drilling two or three holes in a 4 × 4 inch chunk of fencepost, bolting this to the cross-slide, machining the front face with a flycutter (at about 500 ft/min

Fig. 63. The Westbury combined vertical slide, cutter spindle and indexing head. (Photo Woking Precision Models).

and lots of top rake) and then securing the work with woodscrews. (I have been using thick double-sided tape in addition to woodscrews for this type of fixing, with great improvement in the hold). The point

Fig. 64. Facing a cylinder portface using the vertical slide.

39

here is that you have machined the face dead true to the cutter and the rough casting can be secured just as easily on the wood as on metal. The one limitation is that you must not (if using a normal wood) expect the setup to stay true over a period, as moisture in the air will cause the wood to "move". I am fortunate in having a stock of very closegrained wood – Lignum Vitae, Boxwood, etc, – which "stays put" and have even made a permanent machining fixture from Lignum. But I have no hesitation in using a piece of old scaffold-plank if the job can be finished within the day.

GENERAL. In all clamping operations the strength of the workpiece must be kept in mind, and this applies particularly when holding down castings. Even if the base has been filed up a little there is just a risk that the bottom may be concave, convex, or "rockable". Clamping may well cause distortion which will be reflected in the newly machined surface as soon as the clamps are removed. This is an additional reason for using a layer of paper, and if this is reasonably thick and soft it can ease the effects of the odd pimple.

All forms of clamping other than a vice rely on the friction between work and table to resist cutting forces – even with a vice this can be true also. It is prudent to

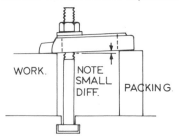

Fig. 65. Correct clamping. The bolt should be as close to the work as possible, and the packing slightly taller than the work.

look at the direction in which these forces will operate and provide a stop-bar or "sprag" to provide a positive location. Sometimes one of the clamp-bolts can serve with a piece of wood between it and the work, but if a tee-slot is conveniently near then a bar dropped in backed by packing is most effective. Note, however, that you must take care that any such stop does not interfere with squaring up work.

I have already referred to the risk with tee-headed bolts, both in stiffening up the slides and of breaking away the edges of the tee-slot. I much prefer the tee-bars, but whichever is to be used it is only reasonable to ensure that as much of the limited clamping force as possible is applied to the work, and least to the packing. Fig. 65 shows the principle, though it has to be accepted that tee-slots seldom come in the right place to allow all bolts to be so sited. Note that the packing should be taller, but only a little taller, than the work. If the reverse applies, the act of clamping can move the work endways.

Workholding and setting up in milling is often a fairly long job – far longer than the actual cutting – and there is the temptation always present to skimp on this part of the process. This must be resisted, as if the work is not sufficiently rigid the result is seldom less than disastrous. The slightest movement of the work allows the cutter to take charge and it will, at best, chew out great chunks of metal in the wrong place and at worse cause actual damage to the machine. If an awkward workpiece cannot conveniently be held it may be necessary first to make a subsidiary workholder. Fig. 66 is a case in point, where a piece of half-inch steel flat has been drilled and tapped on one side to take workholding screws and on the other to secure it to an angleplate. (This is the front view of Fig. 54). Incidentally, this

Fig. 66. A "Subsidiary Workholding Plate". The point in the chuck is used to set up the workpiece on lathe centre-height.

photo shows one way of setting up to centrelines. The point is brought to the marking out lines with the machine running slowly (so that the centre-point runout causes no error) and the work adjusted until it is in line. Note the white-faced backplate which reflects light onto the work.

To deal with the multitude of jigs and fixtures which may be used to hold work would take up a very great deal of room. Indeed, those who have been at it a long time often have a job finding room in the workshop for them! But your own ingenuity will enable you to work them out for yourself when you do come up against the "cannot be held" type of workpiece. Keep the main principles in mind— reference lines or planes to locate the work relative to the axis of the cutter

and, preferably, a further plane or mark from which to establish the correct cutter depth. As I shall emphasise later, it is far better to work to co-ordinates, using feed-screw dials, than to work to marking out lines — provided, that is, that your cutter is not running out. Lines are VERY difficult to see when milling, and it is an unfortunate fact that the set-up on the lathe usually means that your head has to be just where your hair may get caught up in the works. Take this seriously — a few lost hairs may not matter, but "scalped by moving machinery" is an official entry in the Factory Inspector's annual returns. If a rotating cutter-chuck does get hold of your hair it can, quite seriously, take the top of your head off. If you find you can't see properly, keep your head out of the way, and use a mirror. I mean it!

41

CHAPTER 5

Milling Attachments

This title is given to attachments which provide a means of driving a rotating cutter other than the lathe mandrel. (Those which provide means of indexing the work relative to the headstock will be dealt with in chapter 6.) There are two basic types of "Attachment" — those which are normally carried on the saddle, so that the cutter can be moved relative to

Fig. 67. The Potts simple milling spindle.

work held in the normal chuck; and those which are secured to the lathe bed, so that work on the cross-slide can be moved about beneath them. I call the first type "Milling Spindles" to distinguish them from the "Attachment" proper which, in effect, converts the lathe to a small milling machine.

MILLING SPINDLES. These are descendants of the "cutting frames" and "drilling instruments" referred to in the first chapter. Perhaps the best-known is that devised and for decades marketed (both as castings and finished units) by the late Mr. G.P. Potts. Indeed, many model engineers refer to "using the Potts" even though the actual one they own is by Arrand or one of the other makers.*

The basic "Potts" is shown in Fig. 67, though there is usually a pair of adjustable jockey pulleys attached to the body below the drive pulley. That illustrated has the mandrel bored for 8mm collets, but a No. 1 Morse female taper is an alternative. The spindle can be used to carry either milling cutters mounted on arbors or a small drill-chuck.

Messrs Woking Precision Models Ltd, of 16 Dovecote Road, Aberdour, Fife KY3 0TA, bought the patterns from Mr. Potts' executors, and now market the castings.

A more versatile version is shown in Fig. 68. Here the spindle is mounted on its own columnar vertical slide, the column being bolted direct to the cross-slide of the lathe, thus saving the need to mount a normal vertical slide. (The jockeys just referred to can be seen). Other makes are similar except in detail – see Fig 63. A very much more elaborate type is the geared spindle, usually associated with precision lathes and primarily used for gear-cutting, where lower speeds are usually needed. Fig. 69 shows two such, by Lorch; one with a bevel drive, the other with spur gears. These are relatively costly, though many model engineers have built their own. All these spindles need some form of drive mechanism, and this aspect is dealt with later.

The main uses of such spindles is in such work as fluting columns, cutting keyways, drilling rings of holes, machining flats and hexagons on round stock and, of course, cutting gears, ratchets and detents – though many workers make up

Fig. 68. The Potts milling head – the spindle is identical to that in Fig. 67, mounted on the column for height adjustment. (Photo Woking Precision Models).

Fig. 69a. The Lorch direct geared milling spindle. The cutter axis can be set in two positions and can be adjusted as to angle.

Fig. 69b. The Lorch bevel-reduction geared spindle, normally used at or near the vertical.

6. It is also necessary to have some means of vertical movement of the spindle. Those illustrated in Figs 63, 68 and 69 incorporate this in the design, but in other cases attachment to the vertical slide is needed. It is of some importance that the spindle be set at the exact angle. For helical flutes or when thread milling (see page 95) this angle must be calculated from the geometry of the helix.

Fig. 70 shows a number of applications, most of which are self-explanatory

Fig. 70a. Fluting, with the Potts spindle, Fig. 67.

simple cutting frames similar to the Holtzapffel vertical frame shown in Figs. 3 & 4 for this purpose. In all cases some form of indexation of the lathe mandrel is needed, and this is dealt with in Chapter

Fig. 70b. Fluting a long column with the Lorch, Fig. 69b.

Fig. 70c. Combined turning and milling setup. The hexagon is machined part way through the cycle.

taken together with the captions. Some of the photographs have been set up specially for this occasion, and the drive belt has been left off as the driving motor would have obscured either the subject or the background. Fig. 70c is especially interesting. Here the Potts spindle is being used in association with the normal turning operations. The workpiece is a small (5BA) bolt having a collared head. It COULD have been made from hexagon bar with a washer soldered on, but somehow this "did not look right". The bolt is, therefore, turned from round bar and screwed using the tailstock dieholder.

The Potts (not seen) carries a 1/4 inch endmill, and this is traversed across the stock, the headstock being indexed using 60 holes drilled in the chuck backplate. Once the vertical slide is set this can be locked, and the hexagon takes only a few seconds to cut. The work is then parted off. By the use of the topslide index it is possible to follow the procedure on a "production" basis — it was not found necessary to set up any special stops.

SPINDLE DRIVES. An independent drive is needed for any rotary cutting frame, and most people think in terms of the classical "overhead" which was a feature of most amateurs' lathes in the 19th century. Fig. 71 shows one type with the usual drum and jockey pulleys supported on standards. That by Holtzapffel, Fig. 72, could be worked without jockeys, as the spring in the support was usually sufficient. Both suffer from difficulties of inertia and lack of balance, which inhibits the use of any but moderate speeds. Ornamental turners can get over this by using very small pulleys on the cutting frame, but when working metal this leads to belt slip. The idea of the drum was, of course, that the driving belt could move along this as the work was traversed. In fact, however, provided that the driven pulley flanges are reasonable a fair degree of out-of-line can be accepted, usually quite sufficient to deal with most model engineers' applications.

Even in the field of ornamental turning the classical overhead is now seldom used. It is found that a simple jockey system associated with a free-standing electric motor on the back shelf of the lathe meets all needs. This makes the setting up very easy and, moreover, does not lock up the use of a motor; in my case the same motor can be used on three lathes and can also be called upon to drive other plant. The motor itself (1/4 HP,

Fig. 71. The classical "Drum and Jockey" type overhead drive.

which is more than adequate) is fitted with pads of rubber under the feet, and only rarely is it found necessary to bolt it down. This makes belt tensioning easy – it is only necessary to give the motor a push in the right direction.

Fig. 73 shows a very simple spindle drive, described in detail in *Model Engineer* 5 Dec 75, page 1175, and *Simple Workshop Devices*, Argus Books Ltd. The upright is a piece of 5/8 inch (nominal) bore electric conduit, with the bottom couple of inches turned down to fit the socket of the standard Myford handrest bracket. The tee-arm is a piece of $\frac{1}{2}$ inch BDMS brazed into a lump of $1\frac{1}{2}$ inch steel, which is drilled to fit the conduit and fitted with a couple of grub-screws. The pulley bearing block has two holes at right angles to accept the tee

Fig. 72. The standard "Holtzapffel" spring-mounted overhead drum. No jockey is needed.

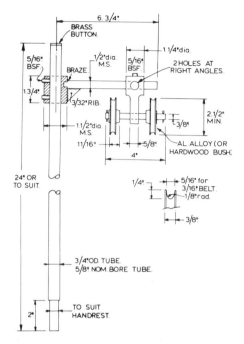

Fig. 73. A simple cutter drive for the Myford.

arm, so that it can be set either way, and carries a pair of 2 inch jockey pulleys retained by split pins. The sketch does not show all the dimensions, as the device can be modified to suit individual needs. The height of the column is relatively unimportant, but if it is made more than 100 times the diameter of the belt normally used this will permit movement of (e.g.) a Potts Milling Spindle over six or eight inches. The one problem may be – "How to machine the end of a two-foot tube when the lathe takes no more than 19 inch between centres?" Easy! Cut off the tube about an inch longer than is needed. Remove the tailstock. Set up the fixed steady at the end of the bed to carry the tube, which is gripped at the other end in the self-centring chuck. Machine the *chuck end* of the tube to the required

dimensions, and then part off close to the chuck! As to the pulleys, there is no need for these to be of metal. Hardwood (Boxwood or Lignum) will serve and as a matter of interest the main drive pulleys on Hotlzapffel No. 484, 180 years old almost, are made of mahogany and the machine is still in use. In many ways wood is better than metal for such applications; but Tufnol is ideal, as it needs no brass bush – it can run directly on the steel spindle.

The group of photographs in Fig. 74 show various arrangements. At (a) the motor sits at the end of the bed and the hand-rest base is clamped to the bed, the Potts being set as if to drill a register of holes. The motor *is* clamped in this case, as the lathebed is narrow At 74(b) the pedestal is clamped to the cross-slide itself and the motor is sitting behind the lathe. This arrangement is suitable when most of the movement is *across* the lathe axis. The full cross-slide travel is possible with no loss of drive power. 74(c) shows the arrangement when most of the travel is *along* the lathe axis; again, the pedestal is clamped to the cross-slide, but behind the vertical slide this time, and the motor sits behind the lathe. The motor has a 4-cone pulley and the speed-range at the spindle runs from well above 3500 rpm down to about 800 rpm.

I use three sorts of belting. Much preferred is 3/16 inch round leather, which gives a good grip and which is heavy enough to drive even if not really tight. Second, almost as good, 1/8 inch (nominal) cotton rope "long spliced" to an endless band. Third, 1/8 or 3/16 inch braided nylon cord, as used for "pull starters" on chainsaws and the like. This can be "welded" in a match or candle flame. It drives fairly well, but has the disadvantage that there is NO stretch, and it is not easy to keep the drive tight if

Fig. 74. The simple overhead drive in use. (a right) Motor on the lathebed. (b below) Motor behind the lathe (c bottom right) Pedestal clamped to saddle.

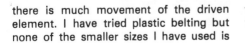

there is much movement of the driven element. I have tried plastic belting but none of the smaller sizes I have used is very satisfactory – chiefly because of its tendency to "whip about".

There are many variations to these

47

drives and some practitioners prefer those with an integral motor. Fig. 75 shows a number of views of a Motorised Drive Unit designed by Mr. J. Malcolm Wild, for which constructional details are given in *Model Engineer* 20 Nov. 81 et seq, starting on page 1382. It will be seen that the motor and an associated countershaft is mounted on the end of a swing arm which can be swivelled into a wide variety of positions. The pillar can either be mounted on the lathe itself or permanently fixed on the bench behind. Toothed vee-belt is used but round leather will serve, at least for the type of application normal for model engineers; Mr. Wild designed the unit primarily for clock-gear cutting. There is a considerable speed range possible due to the countershaft, 6 speeds from 145 to 4150 rpm, though not equally spaced. The motor is 1/8 HP, perhaps a bit on the light side for true milling operations, as there is a fair bit of power loss in the belts and the countershaft and jockey bearings, but quite adequate for its designed purpose. The castings kit is supplied by Mr. J.M. Wild, 12 Norton Green Close, Sheffield S8 8BP.

MILLING ATTACHMENTS. These accessories, either with an integral motor or taking a drive from the lathe headstock, convert the lathe to a true vertical milling machine. The normal movements of the saddle provide transit of the workpiece in

Fig. 75. Various arrangements of the Wild motorised milling cutter drive. (Photos G. Malcolm Wild).

Fig. 76. Improvisation! An arrangement used many years ago by Prof. D.H. Chaddock, shown profile milling a model supercharger casing.

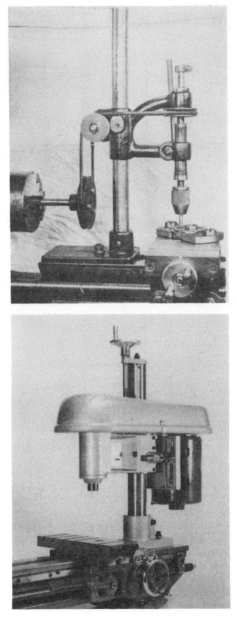

two axes, whilst the movement of the quill or spindle of the attachment adjusts the position of the cutter. The full travel of the cross-slide is available but, unfortunately, the travel possible along the lathe axis is limited by the distance between the quill centreline and the body of the attachment. However, it *is* possible to apply power feed, and this is a considerable advantage; not so much because it saves effort but rather because the cutter very much prefers power feeding!

Fig. 76 shows a fit-up arranged by Mr. (now Professor) Dennis Chaddock some 40-odd years ago, in which he is using his sensitive drill to carry a milling cutter, taking the drive from the lathe headstock. Now, it is true that a drilling machine spindle is not designed to take the side-thrust and it is an unfortunate fact that drill-chucks seldom run dead true. Nevertheless the arrangement is quite practical, and especially for the profile milling job shown in the photo, where the travel of the cutter is limited by a guide or template. (This process is dealt with in more detail on page 109). The main problem with such an arrangement is control of the depth swing of the spindle, and if such a device is used for normal milling great care must be taken to ensure that there can be no inadvertent movement of the quill vertically. Naturally, only very light cuts can be taken.

SELF-POWERED ATTACHMENTS. Fig. 77 shows a milling attachment by Amolco (A.N. Mole & Co., Ltd) intended for use on the tailstock end of the lathe bed. This has a substantial spindle, the nose of which matches that of the Myford lathes, so that

Fig. 77. The Amolco self-contained milling attachment mounted at the tailstock end of the lathe. (Photo A.N. Mole & Co.).

49

Fig. 78. The Myford-Rodney milling attachment, taking power from the lathe headstock. (Photo Myford Ltd).

Autolock or similar chucks, collets, and the usual lathe chucks can be fitted as desired. The spindle is bored for a drawbar. With a 1/4 hp motor and four spindle speeds from 325 up to 1600 rpm reasonable cuts with the normal model engineers' stock of cutters are possible. The limitation is that the "daylight" from spindle centre to column is 5 inches, but this is not all that much less than is found on the smaller ranges of true milling machines. The maximum clearance between the spindle nose and the lathe cross-slide is 8 inches. Vertical travel, by moving the whole of the head on the column, is 6½ inches. One advantage of this type of attachment is that it can be left in place whilst normal turning is in progress provided that the tailstock is not needed. (It is not normally possible to remove a tailstock other than by sliding it off the end of the bed.)

Fig. 78 is the Myford-Rodney milling attachment. This takes its drive from the lathe headstock, so that the cutter speed can be varied over a very wide range by using the back-gear. There are two vertical movements; the main spindle housing or headstock can be moved up and down by about $3\frac{1}{4}$ inches and locked and the spindle or quill carrying the cutter can also be moved about 3 inches. This latter movement can be controlled either by a feed lever for drilling etc, or by a handwheel/worm device for precise setting of milling cutters. The "daylight" between cutter centre and the face of the attachment is $4\frac{1}{2}$ inches and the maximum distance between the spindle nose and the top of the lathe cross-slide is 6 inches. This last dimension will, of course, be reduced by the projection of the cutter. As might be expected, the spindle nose is identical to that on the lathe. A simpler version is available for the ML10 lathe.

Attachments of this type permit milling operations up to the limit of the rigidity of the lathe bed and saddle — and, of course, the available travel of the latter. The motor power available is more than adequate and is not the limiting factor. It is, however, important to keep in mind that the slides are NOT designed for milling work. All movements save that in use for traversing (including the downfeed) MUST be locked whilst cutting and whether using hand or power feed (the latter is strongly recommended) the direction of feed must always be in opposition to the cutting forces. This applies particularly when using the cross-slide feedscrew, as there is always some backlash in the nut. When plunge-cutting (e.g. with a slot-drill) both slides should always be locked. These limitations apart, the use of such attachments does provide an adequate milling facility for the model engineer and will cover almost all his requirements.

GENERAL. It is impossible to detail all the various types of milling "devices" which have been made by model engineers over the years. Their number is legion, and it is difficult to find a volume of the magazine which does not show some example, ranging from the simplest to the fantastic. Excellent work can be done with simple home-made spindles — if cone bearings or even pointed pivots are used there is no difficulty over "slack". Fig. 79 shows a home-made cutting frame with $2\frac{1}{4}/1$ reduction intended for gear-cutting, perhaps 100 years old, and made by a clergyman. This may give some idea of what can be rigged up — they are no less "proper" than the more elaborate devices so far shown.

CHAPTER 6

Indexing and Dividing

References to either of these subjects always seems to invoke visions of complex equipment and abstruse mathematical calculations in the mind of the average model engineer. This is a pity, for the majority of dividing operations required in ordinary work can quite reasonably be described as "Kid's Practice Jobs". False impressions of *required* accuracy are legion; caused in many cases by the fact that the writer of the article has used a complex dividing engine simply for convenience, not because it was necessary. We must keep a sense of proportion in this aspect of model engineering, as in all others. For example, the world will not come to an end if the spanner flats on a workpiece are not machined *precisely* at 120° to each other. If the knob of a 40 tpi. adjusting screw is engraved with 25 divisions, and one is a quarter of a degree out, the positional error caused at the end of the screw is no more than 17 MILLIONTHS of an inch. Naturally, both examples ought to be "done properly", that goes without saying. But you do not need elaborate equipment and the aim should be always to use the simplest set-up that will serve the purpose. If your work involves the cutting of many accurate gears then clearly you will need a proper dividing head with a range of index plates, but if all you ever make in that line is a ratchet for a mechanical lubricator then a simpler, but equally well made, dividing device will serve.

There are two basic methods of carrying out dividing work when milling in the lathe. The preferred method (for all but the lightest jobs) is to carry the cutter on the lathe mandrel and to support the work in an indexable workholder on the saddle. You then have the full speed range of the spindle together with the full power of the motor available for cutting, and it is not difficult to arrange the workholding to suit. There is the added advantage in that all the electrical controls are in an accustomed position. However, there are cases where it is more convenient to use one of the milling spindles already described and to index the work on the lathe mandrel. This is particularly the case when the indexed work is done part way through a normal turning operation. Fig. 70c was a case in point. Again, it is often found that there is not sufficient travel on the cross-slide, especially when fluting columns. So long as the depth of cut and the required cutter speed are within the capacity of the milling spindle one can choose whichever is the most convenient.

There are two main methods of indexing the work, however it may be held, and a few "minor deviations" which occasionally come in handy. I will cover the latter later in the chapter, but the principal methods are either direct dividing (which I tend to call "indexing") and indirect dividing, which involves the use of both a worm and wheel (or other gearing) as well as a division plate – as exemplified in the classical dividing head. Direct dividing requires some "master divider" – it may be a plate with holes in it, a serrated disc, or even a gear-wheel – which has a number of holes or teeth which is a direct multiple of the number of divisions required on the work. It need not be the *same* number of holes; a 60-station master, for example, can index the work for 2, 3, 4, 5, 6, 10, 12, 15, 20, 30 and 60 equally spaced operations. It is surprising how many normal requirements are met by this one number. However, we could not machine (say) 25 flutes with it, and if that number were wanted we should need another plate with (say) 50 or 100 holes.

Suppose we now interpose a 40/1 ratio worm and wheel between the division plate and the work. For 25 divisions we must rotate the worm 40/25 turns to give the required rotation of the workpiece. That is, one whole turn plus 15/25 of a turn. 15/25 = 3/5 = 36/60, so that to index 25 divisions in this case we turn the worm-shaft by 1 complete turn and then 36 holes in the 60-plate further each time. It is a simple as that – though you do need a device on the dividing head to help you remember which holes to use! The reputation for accuracy enjoyed by the dividing head also springs from the use of the worm. Suppose one of the holes in our plate is displaced by one tenth of a degree. With direct dividing that error will be reproduced on the work every time we

use that hole. But it the same plate is used on a dividing head the error is reduced by the worm ratio. With a 40/1 worm the final error is not more than 0.0025 degrees – ten millionths of an inch on a 3 inch pitch circle. Naturally you have to pay for this increased flexibility and improved accuracy – not only in cash. The dividing head occupies a lot of space and can get in the way to a serious extent on a cross-slide. It is much slower in operation, and does need great care both in initial setting and in operation. For these reasons the direct dividing method is the one used for most applications other than gear-cutting or precise engraving (e.g. when making scales on feedscrew indexes). There are those who suggest that a device similar to a rotary table, with a scale marked in degrees – perhaps with a vernier – is more convenient than either form of dividing engine. There are three principal objections. The first is that it is not POSITIVE. The dividing depends on setting two lines together; and even then the setting is not locked as it would be with a plate or detent. Second, the possible divisions are limited to those based on 360 degrees. The "25" division already referred to requires an angular movement of 14

Fig. 79. A home-made gear-cutting frame for use with flycutters.

Fig. 80. Dividing circles on the pulley of a Holtzapffel lathe.

degrees 24 minutes of arc. Third, its operation demands "sequential addition". The example just given means that the successive readings will be 14°–24', 28°–48', 43°–12' etc; a job made more difficult by the fact that the second term goes up in 60's, not decimally. A rotary table CAN be used, very effectively, for "coarse division" work, where precise accuracy is not needed; I use one for fluting taps. But for most work even the direct division plate is superior. (Naturally, if you fit a division plate to a worm shaft driving such a table you HAVE a dividing head).

INDEXING THE HEADSTOCK MANDREL
The classical device is, of course, the

Fig. 81. The micro-adjustment to the index for Fig. 80.

division circle set on the headstock pulley. Fig. 80 shows that on a five-inch lathe of about 90 years ago, but such circles were common right up until the 1930's. They are still found on watchmaker's lathes, of course. There are six rows of holes in Fig. 80, providing 96, 112, 120, 144, 192, and 360 divisions. These cover an incredible range of requirements, as a little work with your calculator will reveal. The index pin has a refinement seen in Fig. 81. There is a calibrated adjustment screw at the anchor point, so that previously machined work can be accurately set to the start of any indexing process. The calibration can

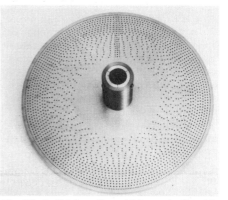

Fig. 82. A dividing disc which can be fitted to the mandrel of a Lorch precision screwcutting (engineer's) lathe.

also (provided you can work it out) enable you to ring changes between one row of holes and the next. Most model engineers will, I am sure, have expressed regret at one time or another that such dividing rings are no longer provided. They forget that all modern machines are fitted with backgear, and unless the lock between pulley and bull-wheel is absolutely positive when in direct drive the backlash errors will be unacceptable.

The "professional" alternative is to secure a separate division plate to the tail of the lathe mandrel when it is needed. Fig. 82 shows a 21-row plate for use on the headstock of a Lorch precision screw-cutting lathe. An expensive attachment, fortunately acquired (second hand) with the lathe, but not used as often as you might imagine. It is *very* difficult to see, let alone count, the holes. Fortunately cheaper and more practical plates are now available for almost any lathe which has a hollow mandrel. Fig. 83 is a photo of one of a range offered by Chronos Designs Ltd, to suit any Myford or Boxford lathe. The plate is secured to a sub-mandrel which has a cone-expanded sleeve to grip

Fig. 83. A Chronos dividing plate fitted to a Myford lathe. (Photo Chronos Ltd).

the inner surface of the hollow headstock mandrel. Some work must be done on the lathe to fit up an index to engage with the holes, but this is not difficult, and the whole system can be fitted and removed quite quickly.

The poor man's alternative is to use change-wheels. The "normal" set provided with any screw-cutting lathe which has no "Norton" gearbox has the disadvantage that they go up in "fives" (25, 30, 35, 40 etc) but the set includes a "60" and other useful sizes are available quite cheaply. Even those who have lathes with a screw-cutting gearbox will, if they are prudent, have a set of wheels to convert to metric — or vice versa. Fig. 84

shows an arrangement which calls for a minimum of setting up. The desired gear is attached to the output stud from the tumbler reverse, and a second gear, on the top stud of the quadrant, is locked by fitting a washer under the retaining nut so that it can act as an index. The photo is

Fig. 84. Dividing using the normal change-wheel train. (See text).

taken on a lathe which *has* a gearbox, and this limits the size of the gear which can be used. However, if the metric conversion quadrant is fitted any gear up to the largest available can be used, and this applies equally to those without gearboxes. There is, however, a rather serious problem when this system is used. The tumbler reverse gears are between the indexing wheel and the lathe mandrel, so

Fig. 85. Mr. Mason's direct division device using lathe changewheels.

that backlash here must be eliminated. In many cases it is sufficient to pull the lathe chuck forward with one hand, but this is a somewhat chancy business. The usual method is to attach a cord to the chuck, wind it round several times and then hang a substantial weight on the end. This is sufficiently effective for the class of dividing for which direct measure from a changewheel is appropriate. There is a second problem with lathes which are "of mature years". The tumbler reverse gears may be worn, and if this wear is uneven then a random error may be introduced into the dividing.

Both these problems can be overcome if the change-wheel is attached

directly to the mandrel itself and a proper detent fitted. The wheel can be fitted with an expanding spindle just as in the case of the Chronos and Lorch plates. The added equipment is all outboard of the normal changewheel system, so that this need not be disturbed; it is put out of action by setting the tumbler reverse in neutral. A full description of such a dividing set-up was given in an article by the late Mr. L.C. Mason in *Model Engineer* of January 16th 1970, and a refinement, providing a much wider range of "numbers" appeared on 20th February 1970. This is about the simplest "purpose made" headstock indexing device that can be built by the model engineer, so that although reproduction is bound to be poor (no original of the photo is available) it is shown in Fig. 85.

In some cases indexing can be done from the *Bull-Wheel* of the back-gear. That on the older ML7 machines had 65 teeth, and this only allows division by 5 and 13, but the Super-7 range and some machines of other makes are fitted with 60T gears. This is a very versatile number, offering 2, 3, 4, 5, 6, 10, 12, 15, 20, 30 & 60 divisions. It is not difficult to arrange an index plunger and Fig. 86 shows my own arrangement, with a sketch of the parts in Fig. 87. When not required the detent lever and spring is removed. It is only a matter of half-a-minute's work to set up and take down. In fact, I use it as as mandrel lock when any milling is needed in the lathe even if no dividing is required., The one important detail is that the detent should bed well down in the space between the teeth. If it beds on the upper part of the tooth flank the curvature can throw it out of mesh.

WORM AND PLATE DIVIDING ON THE LATHE MANDREL

It is, of course, quite possible to attach a normal dividing head to the lathe mandrel, using the expanding spindle already mentioned. However, machines with a 60 or 40 tooth bull-wheel to the back gear contain the bones of a dividing head – all that is needed is a worm and means of holding the counting plate. Those machines with other sizes of bull-wheel present few problems either; even the 65-tooth wheel on the ML7, which factors out at 5 × 13, can be used to index almost all the commonly needed divisions. A very easily made attachment for the Super-7 was described by the late Mr. J. Radford in *Model Engineer* of January 5th, 1968, and a more elaborate design based on the Radford is described by Mr. George Thomas in his book *Dividing and Graduating*. The photo, Fig. 88, shows this one. Mr. Radford used the existing Myford dividing plates, but those supplied today by Chronos Ltd serve well and can also be used on the ML7 65 tooth bull-wheel. Or, of course, you can make your own plates! In his book Mr. Thomas also gives constructional details for a similar head for the ML10. The photos Figs. 89 and 90 show the variations. Mr. Thomas uses a

Fig. 86. Using the back-gear bull-wheel for dividing, on the Author's lathe.

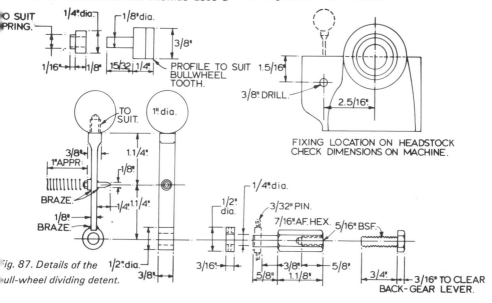

Fig. 87. Details of the bull-wheel dividing detent.

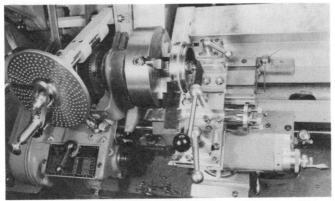

Fig. 88. The Radford worm dividing attachment. (Photo G.H. Thomas).

"Micro-dividing attachment", but this is needed very seldom, and can be omitted with little loss. The main advantage of the device is that once you have made a "60" plate you can use the micro-fitting to develop other numbers from it. It also enables you to divide into certain "prime" numbers normally unobtainable – 127, for example.

I should emphasise again that once a worm is used the difficulties associated with a 65-tooth bull-wheel largely disappear. Naturally the 60-ratio plates will not serve, but others will, and in fact, Messres Chronos will shortly be able to supply plates specially to fit this ratio. However, the table in the appendix shows that even with their standard plates most useful numbers below 100 as well as 120, 125 and 360 can be provided for.

UNORTHODOX METHODS. From the sublime to the ridiculous! I have already implied that elaborate methods are not always needed. Take the case of the

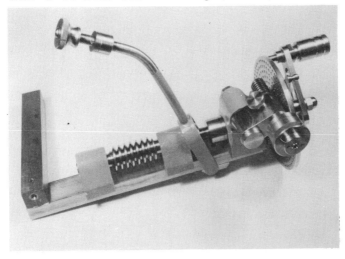

Fig. 89. The Radford unit separated from the lathe (Photo G.H. Thomas).

cylinder cover which needs 9 holes on a pitch circle. If the cover is used (as usual) as a jig to drill the mating holes in the cylinder, "dividing head" accuracy is not needed. Further, the drilling process requires very little restraining force on the workholder – if the lathe is in back-gear and the drive belts on the lowest speed this will effectively hold the mandrel once it is indexed. If the work is held in the 3-jaw chuck we can index for three of the holes by setting a simple spirit level on each jaw in turn. To obtain the inter-mediate holes we must index round 40° each side of these holes. This is readily done by using a protractor level, Fig. 91. For any other number of holes the appropriate setting of the protractor can be worked out, but for those which are not multiples of three care must be taken to set the protractor the right way round. This method – either for marking out or for drilling with the Potts spindle – gives perfectly acceptable results for such applications.

My second example refers to the 25 divisions needed for an adjusting knob for

Fig. 90. The G.H. Thomas bull-wheel dividing attachment (Photo G.H. Thomas).

Fig. 91. Dividing using the chuck jaws and a protractor square.

59

Fig. 92. A saddle-mounting dividing spindle for 10mm collets. The head has 60 teeth.

a 40tpi screw. (25 divisions are required for an advance of one thou per division.) Set up the lathe to cut 8 tpi – the same pitch as the leadscrew, so that the gear ratio between lathe mandrel and leadscrew is unity. Wind a cord round the chuck and hang a substantial weight on the end to take up backlash in the change-wheel train. The necessary 25 divisions are obtained by turning the chuck – always in the same direction – until the

Fig. 93. The G.H. Thomas direct dividing attachment (Photo G.H. Thomas).

leadscrew handwheel index, which has 125 divisions, is set at each "five" on the wheel. With reasonable care this will give pretty accurate dividing and, as I have already pointed out, slight errors are insignificant' as they are divided by 40 owing to the pitch of the adjusting screw.

To conclude this section, you will notice in some of the photos (e.g. Figs. 113 and 86) that one of my chuck backplates is drilled with 60 division holes. The index, unfortunately, cannot be seen, as it is at the back of the machine, secured by a stud in the hole provided by Myfords for the chuck-guard. This is a preferred alternative to indexing on the bull-wheel, but unfortunately not all chucks have backplates and in any case it cannot be used on the 4-jaw independent chuck. There is ample room for two sets of holes, and were I doing the job again I would set up for 120 and 96, which covers almost all work that I do. The holes themselves were, I confess, drilled using my proper dividing head in a milling machine, but there are other methods, covered in part by the next section.

INDEXING ON THE SADDLE. Here again we have the choice of direct or geared indexing, and I need not go through the discussions again, but concentrate on "appliances". Fig. 92 shows a very simple indexing head by Lorch. The division disc is furnished with 60 vee-shaped slots in the periphery, and the spring-loaded lever has a detent which matches them. The workholder is a 10mm collet, shown in the photo with an arbor for carrying gear blanks. This type of head is typical of most home constructed devices. The details vary but the principle is the same. The hollow mandrel may, of course, be finished to match the lathe mandrel so that chucks can be used. The important points of construction are that the mandrel be a good fit to the body and that there must be no end-float. The indexing head is normally fitted to a vertical slide.

A very similar design is the "Simple" or "Basic" dividing head designed by Mr. George Thomas, shown in Fig. 93. This employs a disc with 24 holes as the master – the gear teeth are provided for the head when "developed" into a more elaborate type mentioned later. This unit has two interesting features. First, the workholding concept is that of a plain bored hole, into which any other device may be fitted. Second, though not shown in the photo, a "tailstock" can be carried on a bar secured through a bored hole in the body of the head – a useful refinement.

Reference has already been made to the combined vertical slide and milling spindle designed by the late Mr. E.T. Westbury and marketed in casting form by Woking Precision Models Ltd. (Fig. 63). This has provision for service as an

Fig. 94. The Westbury vertical slide indexing device. See also Fig. 63 (Photo Woking Precision Models).

Fig. 95. The M.E.S. dividing spindle (Photo Model Engineering Services).

61

indexing head and Fig. 94 shows the "business end". Change wheels are used as the master, and the detent is so arranged that any size can be fitted.

Still using changewheels but this time with provision for "geared indexing" is the Direct Division head for which castings are marketed by Model Engineering Services Ltd., Fig. 95. The photo shows the deterent engaged with the 60-tooth "direct" gear, which is carried on a mandrel which duplicates that of the Myford range of lathes. This detent is interesting, as it can be engaged either *between* two teeth or ON a tooth – in effect, giving half-pitch dividing and enabling the 60-t wheel to behave as if it had 120 teeth. The 60-t wheel on the main spindle meshes with a 20-tooth pinion on a stub carrying a further 60-tooth wheel. If the detent is moved from the position shown in the photo to the other arm the 3/1 gear ratio is introduced, giving the effect of a 180 division master – or 360 divisions allowing for the double action of the detent. The head is shown

mounted on a raising block in the photo, but it can be carried on a vertical slide and as the unit is "single-bolt fixing" it can be set at any desired angle. A device such as this can be used to carry a chuck backplate to drill the holes referred to previously, for lathe headstock indexing.

THE DIVIDING HEAD. This is essentially for use on the saddle, even though "worm heads" on the headstock are very little different. That for the saddle has the usual division plate and worm, but also has some means of carrying a mini-tailstock, so that long work can be supported at both ends. The only limitation to the length of the work is the travel of the cross-slide – and the space occupied by the head. They can be mounted directly on the cross-slide or, more usually, on either the plain or swivelling vertical slide. The latter is necessary when work of any great diameter is to be machined. The work is almost always set above the cutter-mandrel when gear-cutting.

Fig. 96 shows the well-known Myford dividing head. This is provided with a 60-1

Fig. 96. The Myford dividing head mounted on the Myford raising block (Photo Myford Ltd.).

Fig. 97. Rear view of a Myford head, showing the worm wheel.

worm and comes with two plates which cover a very wide range of divisions. (Extra plates can be had which cover the awkward prime numbers and their products). The body or base is furnished with a key which is a close fit to the slots on cross- and vertical slides, and the tailstock is mounted on a detachable overarm, making the head self-contained in this mode. The spindle matches the lathe headstock and is bored to accept through work or a drawbar into the No. 2 Morse taper socket. The head may be set with the work axis either along or across the lathe bed and, with the swivelling slide, at any angle to these as well as at vertical angles. Gear wheels up to about $6\frac{1}{2}$ inch diameter can be cut if care is taken not to overload the mounting — several passes may be needed at this large diameter. The vertical slide must, of course, be mounted on a raising block in such a case. Fig. 97 shows the unit mounted for cutting a small gear and using vertical slides and raising block.

The Versatile Dividing Head designed by Mr. George Thomas is similar in principle to the Myford, but has a number of refinements. The basis is the simple head shown in Fig. 93, with the addition of a 60/1 worm reduction, Fig. 98, and

Fig. 98. The G.H. Thomas "Versatile" dividing head. (Photo G.H. Thomas).

like the Myford it also has a tailstock carried on an overarm (Fig. 99). However, it can be used either for direct indexing on the 24 tooth detent or through the worm reduction. In addition, the "micro" device permits the rotation of the dividing plate itself so that it is possible to index "between holes" as it were. The plates themselves are smaller than those of the Myford, but this is not necessarily a disadvantage. Being home constructed (castings etc are available from N.S. & A. Hemingway, 30 Links View, Rochdale OL11 4DD) modifications can be made to suit individual needs. The original articles describing the construction, first printed in *Model Engineer*, are now available as a book from Argus Books Ltd. The one

Fig. 99. The "Versatile" head set up with a tail-centre (Photo G.H. Thomas).

limitation from my point of view is that the dividing head mandrel is not equipped to take lathe-chucks, and as I do a lot of dividing as an "intermediate process" when turning this could be a nuisance.

PROCEDURE. This is far simpler than most people imagine; it is only when very large numbers are required that complications arise. The work is more one of selection – of the best wheel or row of holes – and the word "best" should really be replaced by "most convenient". There is, however, one reservation which I must put before you. If we need 20 divisions then the most convenient number to use *IS* 20; no counting is involved, as we just hop from one tooth or hole to the next. This makes "human error" very unlikely. But, if one tooth is in error, due to damage or wear, we cannot avoid it. If, instead, we use the 60 wheel this chance is reduced – and if we *know* that one tooth gap is faulty we need not use it. I confess that I tend to use 60 tooth change-wheels or 120 hole plates in preference to smaller ones all the time, with my 96-hole plate coming hard on their heels. So, let us look at the facilities available.

DIVISION PLATES ON THE HEADSTOCK
The table below shows the divisions that can be achieved with the plates found on pulleys on the older lathes, and may give some indication as to those which might be used if you are making a plate to attach to the mandrel. Note that these are directed more to "engineering" services than to horology, but they meet a good deal of that also.

It will be noted that the three "high number" rows only add 13 further divisions, and the 112 row really adds only the factors of 7. The 360 hole plate is always difficult to use, as the holes are so close together. The 192 plate adds only divisions of 32, 64 and 192 to those available on the 96. So, for this type of

TABLE I

No. of Holes in circle

96		112	120	144	192	360	360
2	(180)	2	2	2	2	2	
3	(120)	4	3	3	3	3	
4	(90)	7	4	4	4	4	
6	(60)	8	5	6	6	5	
8	(45)	14	6	8	8	6	
12	(30)	16	8	12	12	8	
16		28	10	18	16	10	
24	(15)	56	12	24	24	12	45
48		112	15	36	32	15	60
96			20	48	48	18	72
			24	72	64	20	90
			30	144	96	24	120
			40		192	30	180
			60			36	360

(The figures in brackets in the 96 column are angles in degrees)

division, 96 and 120 will cover a great deal of the numbers needed by model engineers, and provide the most common "engineering angles" as well. The main problem found with this type of division plate is the actual "counting". It *is* possible to make a "counting index" and most practitioners who own one always are keen to show it off. But I find a much simpler way is to mark the holes I need with a felt pen — the mark rubs off easily with a little methylated spirit!

DIRECT INDEXING WITH CHANGEWHEELS

As already observed, the difficulty here is that the normal standard set goes up in "fives", plus the 38 in most cases. Nevertheless, a considerable amount of dividing can be done with these. But there is a total of 40 wheels available in the Myford catalogue and a similar number for other makes, so that the range can be extended considerably if need be. If the index detent is made so that it will both go between teeth *and* sit on top of each tooth, then the possible number of divisions is extended further. I must, however, warn you that the notch to accept the gear tooth MUST be made with the *utmost* care, otherwise it will not be of any use at all — rather the reverse. Any error here will be transferred to the workpiece at each alternate division.

The usual "normal set" of wheels is — 20, 25, 30, 35, 38, 40, 45, 50, 55, 60, 65, 70 and 75. The change-wheels provided for the metric conversion set for lathes with a *gearbox* which has an 8tpi leadscrew are 28, 30, 35, 40, 45, 50, 55, 60 and 63. In the Appendix II I show the wheels which can be used for divisions within the total range. The first wheel shown is the one that I would use, with second and third preferences following in some cases. Wheels in brackets are available, but not normally part of the standard set. However, many turners will choose to include a 21, a 63, or a 127 wheel for metric pitches when they buy their lathe, and these are shown with a star. Divisions in the larger numbers are possible only with a wheel of the same number, so that for figures above 45 I have shown only the divisions that can be accomplished — the wheel is the same as the number. The exception is 50, which can, of course, be obtained from the 100 wheel as well. These divisions are, of course, possible whether the wheel is set on the headstock mandrel or on a dividing engine on the saddle. If this accessory has a compound train — like the 3/1 arrangement on the M.E.S. dividing head shown in Fig. 95 — all that is necessary is to divide the desired number of divisions by three and refer the result to the table in order to ascertain whether this division is possible. In the case of the MES head, of course, the primary wheel is a "sixty" so that only those numbers for which 60 is a "possible" after dividing by three can be accommodated. e.g. 36/3 = 12, which will "go" but 39/3 = 13 which will not.

The procedure, then, is quite simple. Check the table to find the wheels (or the ring of holes if a plate is being used) which will serve and select the most convenient. If the intervals between teeth needed for indexing is fairly large, mark them with a felt pen. In the case of a hole-plate I usually try to start the operation at the "zero" hole – the zero of all rings is usually on a straight radial line – so that I can check by using the engraved numbers on the row. Make sure that the detent engages properly, and if the indexing is being done through any chain of gears, such as the tumbler reverse, make some arrangements to take up the backlash. Finally, when indexing ALWAYS approach the next station from the same direction; if you go too far you must go back by several teeth or holes, and then come forward again. I need not emphasise the need to be sure that the dividing engine is set square (or at the appropriate angle) to the axis of the cutter spindle. This is very important indeed. If cutting a gearwheel any error here will result in the teeth being on the skew, whilst if the set-up is being used (e.g) for making a further division plate the ring of holes will be an ellipse, and faulty dividing will be inevitable whenever it is used.

INDEXING WITH A DIVIDING HEAD. I have already outlined the principle. The gear ratio of the head is divided by the number of divisions required, the resulting fraction is first simplified, and then the fractional part is re-calculated so that the bottom deck coincides with one of the plates. It is much easier to show this by a couple of examples. Thus:

(i) Gear Ratio 60/1. Required divisions 16. Plate with 32, 34, 38, 45, 49, 77 holes.

$60/16 = 3 + 12/16 = 3 + 3/4 = 3 + 24/32$

The handle is turned through three complete revolutions and then 24 holes further on the 32-hole row of the plate.

(ii) Gear Ratio 40/1. Required divisions 52. Plate 37, 39, 41, 43, 47, 49.

$40/52 = 10/13 = 30/39$.

The handle is turned through 30 holes in the 39-hole plate.

(iii) Gear Ratio 60. Required division 12. Plates as above

$$60/12 = 5.$$

ANY row of holes can be used, as the division is made by making five full turns of the handle each time.

(iv) To Index in Degrees.

There are two approaches. The first is to find the index interval corresponding to one degree and then "multiply up". This, for a 60/1 ratio, will be 60/360 = 1/6. A row of holes must then be found which can be divided by six. On the Myford standard plates this will be 42, so that one degree = 7/42. Then, for (say) 125 degrees we must index by 125 × 7/42 = 875/42 = 20 + 35/42, which is 20 whole turns plus 35 holes on the 42-hole row.

The second approach is to note that with a 60/1 ratio one complete revolution of the handle moves the work 6 degrees. Then, for the example above 125/6 = 20 + 5/6 = 20 + 35/42, as before. This method is the most useful when dealing with "odd angles". To take another example, this time with a 40/1 ratio, required to index through 24°36'. One turn of the handle moves the work through 9° (360/40 = 9)

$$\frac{24°36'}{9} = \frac{24\frac{3}{5}}{9} = 2 + \frac{6\frac{3}{5}}{9} = 2\frac{33}{45}$$

$$= 2\frac{11}{15} = 2\frac{22}{30}$$

So, we must turn the handle two full turns and then either 33 holes on the 45 row, 11 holes on the 15 row, or 22 holes on the 30 row, depending on which is convenient – or available. This is a Cincinnati head, and the only one of these available is the 30.

Which of these methods is used is a matter of choice. For small angular movements the first is usually the most convenient – it is fairly easy to remember (or make a note) that on a Myford 60/1 head one degree is 7 holes on the 42 circle.

There will always be divisions which cannot be executed unless special plates are made. These are usually prime numbers (53, 59, 61, for example) or larger multiples of primes. Thus 11, 22, 33, 44, 55, 66, 77 – all multiples of 11 – may be possible, but not 88, 99, or higher. The smaller ones can be done with 77 holes on a 60/1 head. A 66-hole row can do the larger numbers but not all of the smaller ones. The designers of division plates endeavour to meet the MOST COMMONLY NEEDED intervals with as few rows as possible for cost reasons. It is, for example, not really economic to include an 83-hole row when the only divisions it can be used for are 83, 166, 249 . . . etc! It IS possible to use what the ornamental turners call "Double counting" by using double-sided plates with different rows on each side and indexing both the plate itself and the operating handle, but this method lies far outside the scope of this book. The model engineer will find that he has ample provision on the plates normally supplied with commercial dividing heads, and if he is making the Versatile Dividing Head he may well find that he is encouraged to be satisfied – making dividing plates is a time consuming job!

PROCEDURE. As before, the utmost care must be taken in setting up, especially when the tailstock overarm is in use. The vertical slide must be "clocked" truly square to the machine and the head itself then checked likewise. (The vertical slide is going to provide one of the movements and also supports the base of the head). Although the base of the head may be provided with a key or glut fitting the tee-slots, squareness in this direction should always be checked. Setting the overarm should preferably be done with a parallel test-bar set between centres. Fortunately the arbor on which the work is to be mounted will often serve, but if this is a taper mandrel it will be necessary to allow for the taper.

Fig. 100. Use of the sector arms. (a) Cutting. (b) Index moved to the next division position. (c) Sector arms moved; all ready for the next cut.

The divisions having been worked out (tables will be found in the Appendix) the work should be set up so that if at all possible cutting can commence with the index in the "zero" hole. The radius arm must be adjusted so that the detent drops cleanly into the holes and fits snugly. To assist in "counting" all heads are furnished with "sector arms". These are seen on most of the photos, but I have shown them in Fig. 100. The arms are set to provide for indexing four holes on the 32 row – the smallest. At (a) the cut is being made with the index in the first hole. At (b) the control arm has been moved to meet the lower sector arm, – the sector arms are (or should be) stiff enough to avoid accidental movement, but if at all slack they should be held firmly whilst moving the operating control arm. BEFORE CUTTING STARTS the sector arms are then moved to the position shown at (c), which leaves them ready for the next operation. This drill should be followed always and will soon become automatic. Cutting should always take place with the trailing arm in contact with the detent pin. (If the control handle is being rotated in the opposite direction, then the sector arms should be on the opposite side, of course).

Two points should be noted. First, we are indexing *spaces*. "Four Holes" means four spaces. It follows that the sector arms will actually span FIVE holes. Second, despite all the precautions taken by the manufacturer (you, if you have made it yourself!) there is bound to be just a little backlash in the worm. There is – or should be – sufficient friction in the workholding spindle to prevent it from moving under the cut, but you MUST always approach the setting hole from the same direction. If you overshoot you must go back several holes and try again. This is an imperative in all dividing.

WORKHOLDING WHEN DIVIDING. We have already looked at workholding generally, but there are one or two special conditions which arise when any dividing is to be done. Clearly, if the workpiece is carried between centres there must be some means of ensuring that it "stays in register". The carriers used in industry engage with forked catchplates which have some form of setscrew to ensure that there is no radial play – Fig. 101. It may not be necessary to go to such lengths, but you should aim at some device which will serve the same purpose. Simply tying the carrier to the catchplate is not really sufficient.

The next problem arises from the fact that the cutter may interfere with the carrier or chuck before reaching the end of the required travel. This can be a real nuisance when fluting columns. This must be foreseen in the roughing stage (or, better, during the design of the model) and I always leave extra length on the stock to act as a chucking or holding piece. Even if collets are used the nosepiece does get in the way if the cutter is of any size. This is, incidentally, one reason why I tend to use slot-drills rather than wheelform cutters. If one end of the work is held in the chuck and the other on the tailstock centre the chuck run-out should be corrected. True, the "odd thou" may not seem to matter, and if the work is that of fluting a tap or reamer it won't, but if it is a fluted column again then the error may be visible to the discerning eye.

I have already referred to the need for absolute truth and squareness but there are occasions when taper work is needed. If this is to be machined with a Potts spindle with the work in the lathe centres, don't forget that the cutter must be in front of the workpiece (or behind) and *not* on top! The set-over tailstock only moves the centre sideways. If the work is held in the indexing attachment on the saddle the problem is easier – it is only necessary to clock the rough-turned blank to adjust the angle of the vertical slide to suit.

CONCLUSION. I will end much as I started. The *simplest* dividing set-up which will provide the number of divisions is always the best. There is absolutely NO need to invest in a complex dividing head unless you are going to make gears in quantity – or at least, as a regular thing. Even then, a simple indexing device with direct division (plates or wheels) may well serve. I have already shown that the fact that your bull-wheel is an awkward tooth number need not worry you; in fact, if it were some impossible number like 73 teeth division over a considerable range would be possible with no special plates. *Direct* division would not be possible, but worm division would

Nor need you be too concerned about division plates. Mr. Thomas shows one method of initiating plates in his book; there are others, but even if you feel this work to be beyond you the Chronos plates are relatively cheap, and once you have one plate you can always use it to make others if you fit a worm to your headstock. If you have fought shy of models which

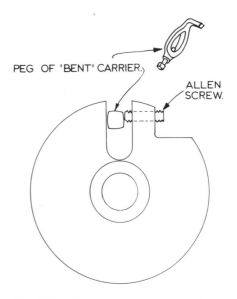

PEG OF 'BENT' CARRIER.

ALLEN SCREW.

Fig. 101. Modified catchplate, to take up backlash on carrier when dividing.

involve dividing I suggest that you take the bull by the horns and have a try. You may be surprised how easy it is once you have a bit of practice. But – you *must* keep your mind on the job; distractions can easily cause you to lose count.

CHAPTER 7

Procedures and Case Studies

Procedures vary so widely that the best approach seems to be to deal first with a few very general points and then to look at a number of actual examples. So much depends on the individual needs of the practitioner and even more on the facilities available when using a lathe as a miller, and this means that you will have to adapt your methods to the work in hand. It is surprising what *can* be done; many years ago I saw some large diesel engine crankshafts, with 6 throws, pins 6 inches diameter, which had been made entirely by milling – crankpins and journals included. True, this needed some rather special rigs, but it is not beyond the capabilities of the amateur – though I doubt whether anything would be gained over the normal method. The milling process is normally used for making flat surfaces, so let us look at this first.

In Fig. 44, page 27, I showed the "design" cutting depths for an endmill, and in the nature of the lathe it is normally the end mill or the shell endmill that we should use for surfacing. If a lot of metal is to be removed then the cutter can be fed in by the required depth for the roughing cut and "run round" the work as shown in Fig. 102, using the cross-slide and vertical slide feeds in turn. Do not forget to lock

the one whilst the other is used. The feed is, of course, run *against* the rotation of the cutter. The cut is continuous, and the maximum amount of metal is removed in the minimum time. If the depth of cut is relatively shallow then the width may be increased somewhat, but never beyond half the cutter diameter; you will find the action distinctly unhappy if the teeth are cutting "backwards" as it were. The feed rate should be kept up, and if you find that there are signs of overloading then the depth of cut should be reduced, not the feed rate. Further, if the cutter is not as sharp as it might be it is better to use a slightly higher feed rate than a lower. Blunt cutters will not cut if the feed rate is too low. The teeth will rub and blunt the cutter still further.

CUTTING FLUID. All roughing operations will generate a good deal of heat and some form of coolant supply is desirable. However, there is quite a difference between the state of affairs when turning. It is often sufficient simply to keep the work "wet" when turning but this would be fatal in a milling operation. The damp chips will form a mush which clogs the clearance spaces and tends to wedge under the teeth. The flow must be sufficient to *wash away* the chips and this can present problems. My own coolant system can give a good flow from gravity feed, but the "tank" holds no more than a pint and refilling is frequent. For most of my work, therefore, I tend to reduce the cut to a depth that permits working dry. Both turning and milling come in the range of operations where "cooling" is more important than "lubrication" and a plain soluble oil is more effective than neat cutting oils. There should be no need for model engineers to use "EP" (Extreme Pressure) cutting fluids but in view of the very intermittent use made of the machine it IS important to specify good anti-rust properties. As a rule this means no more than taking care of the mixing and storage. The coolant should only be mixed up "as required" – not kept stored for long periods in the mixed state. *The oil should be added to the water* with constant, preferably mechanical, stirring. In service the fluid should be cleaned periodically – the presence of chippings, especially fine ones, causes degradation of the emulsion. This is particularly a problem with model-making, as the swarf-tray can contain particles of many different metals. I must confess that although the soluble oil emulsion is far the best coolant for our work I always use a "neat" cutting oil – one *designed* for use neat, not an undiluted soluble oil, which won't work at all.

FINISHING. As already observed, the depth of the finishing cut should be a CUT – less than 0.003" to 0.005" is likely to result in rubbing. This means that the cutter must be sharp. This is covered in the next chapter, but often a slight stoning of the edges will serve – unless you can afford to keep a cutter specially for finishing! At these light cuts the endmill can be worked at up to 7/8 of the full width. It may be traversed round and round as in Fig. 102 or with repeated

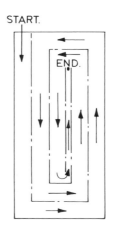

START.
END.

Fig. 102. Path of cutter to avoid any "idle time".

traverses, but the feed must still always be against the rotation of the cutter. If the work is narrower than the cutter – as when using a shell end-mill – then the greater overlap should be on the trailing side.

Now a word about the use of FLYCUTTERS for surfacing. I know that many use flycutters in preference to endmills or facing cutters even though these are available, on the grounds that they get a "better finish". The work certainly looks "smoother" if the cutter sweeps right across, but this is deceptive. Fig. 103 shows the face of a cast-iron test block, of 215 Brinell hardness, 4 inches long by $1\frac{3}{4}$ inch wide, machined with a $\frac{1}{2}$-inch end mill, the overlap between cuts being $\frac{1}{8}$-inch. The cutter was in "reasonable" condition – not "new" but with a good cutting edge. At "a" the surface has been machined cross-ways and "b" is the other (slightly wider) side machined endways. Despite appearances the surface at "a" is

71

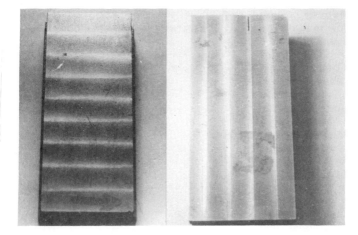

Fig. 103. (a left) This surface is flat within 0.0001 inch. (b right) The opposite side of 103a, flat within 0.0004 inch. See text.

flat within 1/10th of a thou, and that at "b" is no more than 4 tenths "wavy". This latter result is worse than the other because the cutter axis was not dead square to the work. In both cases the "smoothness" is better than 60 micro-inches (millionths of an inch) CLA; This would be classed as a very fine machined finish indeed and is about the average finish expected from surface GRINDING.

Now consider the time taken. The cutter was run rather fast, but 480 rpm (62 ft/min) is not excesive for a finishing cut. The tooth load was 0.0015 in, so that with 4 teeth the time taken to traverse across the work ("a") was 6.87 minutes (the cutter must clear the work both ends, so that $\frac{1}{2}$ inch has to be added to the width). "Winding back" time and the time taken to traverse the cutter was 32 seconds, so, with nine cuts "idle time" totals 4.8 min. The total to finish the surface was just over $11\frac{1}{2}$ minutes. For "b" the total was just over $9\frac{1}{2}$ minutes – less because there is less idle time. Compare this with a HSS fly-cutter run at the same cutting speed, requiring 100 rpm. We should cut longitudinally, of

course (as at "b") and the cutter again has to clear the workpiece. To cover the area we should need a cutter $2\frac{1}{4}$ inch effective diameter, and the tooth load cannot be greater than 0.003 inch if reasonable finish is to be achieved. So, at 100 rpm and $6\frac{1}{4}$ inch total travel the time taken works out at just under 21 minutes. (If we used the same tooth load this would be around 41 minutes!)

Whether you could wind the handle so slowly and keep it steady (unless you had power cross feed) is doubtful, so that the surface finish could well be worse. But there is another factor. The cutter in case "b" was not, in fact dead square to the work traverse; this was done on purpose to see the effect, but would be unavoidable if traversing across the lathe, for reasons we have already discussed. (Case "b" is the equivalent of a VERTICAL feed direction on a lathe). The error on a cutter $2\frac{1}{4}$ inch dia would be $2\frac{1}{4}$ thou or a little more – the work would be taper by that amount. In addition, it would also be slightly hollow.

In short, the flycutter does not save time; to complete the work in the same time as case "b" we should need a tooth load of at least ten thou/rev, which is hardly a finishing cut, even with a round-nose tool. The finish, even at the proper tooth load, is likely to be worse, for we do not have the end faces of the endmill to "shave off" the tool-marks. And there is more probability of geometrical error. To say this is not to deprecate the use of fly-cutters altogether. There are situations where an end-mill cannot be used. And, I expect, many more cases where there is literally no end-mill in the shop — such cutters are expensive, and many readers will, quite wisely, spend their money on slot-drills for essential purpose, where nothing else will do. (Port milling etc). But it is a mistake to assume, as many do, that the large diameter flycutter is BETTER than an end-mill, when dealing with large surfaces.

PROFILING AND "SLAB" CUTTING. The cut here is taken entirely by the teeth on the cylinder of the cutter. Two difficulties seem to be common. The first is "waviness" of the surface. This is due more often than not to cutter runout — e.g. if held in a 3-jaw chuck without correcting the error. If a holder of the Autolock type is not available and you have no master-slave chuck suitable you may find an improvement by setting the cutter in the 4-jaw and trueing it up in the ordinary way. It is no use trying to reduce the effect by reducing the feed rate, for this will certainly lead to other troubles. But a common cause is bell-mouthing of the chuck jaws and this can sometimes be mitigated by using a piece of drawing-paper round the cutter shank at the mouth of the jaws. The other most common cause is lack of rigidity, and this can be a particular problem if, due to the nature of the work or the workholder, the cutter has to be set with a long projection — or a "long" series cutter has to be used. This is

one situation where a reduction in feed rate MAY help — provided the cutter is sharp — but do not go below 60% of that recommended in Chapter 3. However, before doing anything else look over the set-up for lack of rigidiy and, if possible, stiffen things up a bit. You will see in a later example that I have used a little screw jack to support work, for this reason.

The second difficulty which can arise is dragging on the surface; this appears almost as if the metal had been "pulled up by the roots" instead of being properly "cut". It can happen on both heavy roughing cuts and on light finishing ones too; reducing the cut is not necessarily a cure. The first (and with the model engineer the most probable) cause is a blunt cutter. If you have no means of sharpening it, and stoning the edge does not help, try (if it is possible) to use a part of the cutter nearer the shank end, which will have had much less use. The second cause is too LOW a feed rate. It may be that you have misjudged (or mis-calculated) the necessary rate of turning the handle, or set the wrong wheels in place if you are fortunate enough to have a power traverse. Check this. But the tooth loads given on page 26 are not the laws of the Medes and Persians, and if you do have this trouble try feeding faster. What is happening is that chips are getting wedged between the teeth and the work, and interfering with the proper cutting action. The effect with a blunt tooth is obvious — it doesn't "cut"; an increased feed-rate increases the thickness of the chip and reduces the risk. Incidentally, if you are using coolant, try either shutting it off or, better, increasing the rate of flow A LOT. It might help!

Though perhaps not of much help to readers who have only a limited number of cutters it does help to get a better finish if, when in a situation where a relatively light depth of cut is being taken, you can use either a cutter with more teeth, or one with a steeper helix when all the cutting is being done by teeth on the cylinder. An improvement may occasionally be effected by changing to a cutter of different diameter, too. This is especially effective when one finds that only one tooth is in contact — there is a tendency when hand feeding for the work to make a little jerk forwards between teeth. Again, power feed makes a big difference.

SLOTTING. I have, I think, already made the main points already. Use a slot-drill, *not* an end-mill, even if you can enter the slot from the end. If you have no slot drill the correct size, make a central slot with a smaller one and then machine each side singly with an endmill. You CANNOT get a good finish on both sides of a slot when an end-mill is cutting full face — though the new Clarkson three-flute end-mills *can* be used for either purpose. These are "Premium" H.S. Steel and rather expensive, but as they double for two cutters perhaps not too dear. Fig. 104 shows one in action (on a milling machine) both in slotting and profiling. It is a larger version

Fig. 104. A ½in. 3-flute endmill which can also serve as a slot drill. (Photo Clarkson International).

of the FC3 "Throwaway" type cutter — which are available only up to ¼ inch dia against the ¾ inch for the larger type.

When using a slot drill it is more than ever necessary to ensure that the cutter is running true, and a master chuck, or a proper adaptor with No. 2 Morse taper and drawbar, is an essential if accurate slots are requried. Naturally, Autolock or similar can be relied upon in this respect, but the use of the ordinary self-centring 3-jaw should be avoided unless the width of the slot is not critical to a couple of thou or so. I always prefer to slot full depth at one pass if at all possible, within the limits of Fig. 44 page 27. There is, even with the best of holders, always a risk of widening the slot at the top if a second pass is made. Chip clearance is especially important, and if you have to use coolant use a flood. Or, if you are not getting any heating, you can perhaps blow the chips away with compressed air, but USE GOGGLES if you do this; milling chips are VERY sharp at one end!

SLITTING SAWS can be used to cut slots as well as to cut off material to accurate length. Accurate alignment is very important, as any skewness will cause the saw to bind. Rigid workholding is also important, as any movement may break the saw or worse. True, one can use small, fine-tooth saws on a plain saw-table with no more than hand grip on soft material but this should never be done when the cutting forces are of any magnitude. The biggest difficulty seems to be that many model engineers have been supplied with saws of far too great a tooth pitch. I shall show at least one example of this later, but you should take it as a general rule that there should always be three teeth actually cutting at once. Again, power feed reduces the problem; with hand feeding there is the tendency for the work to jump into the cut between teeth, already mentioned. The rule about "floods of coolant or none" applies particularly to saws, where the risk of chips wedging in the cut, if not chokng the gullets, is considerable.

SOME CASE STUDIES

I think I have already made it clear that the field is so wide that it would be impossible to cover every eventuality. In the following I have tried to show examples which are "representative" and which may give clues to other applications. In many cases I have had to set up specially to provide examples which I had not photographed when done originally, and I am particularly grateful to Messrs Stuart Turner Ltd who very kindly supplied me with some engine castings to "chew up for your edification"! Let us start with a simple case.

TEE-SLOT BAR, Fig. 105. The vertical slide is first set dead square across the bed, and the jaws of the vice then checked for parallelism horizontally. The stock is $\frac{1}{2}$ inch × 5/16 inch, and the centre part of the tee is to finish 5 thou under 3/8 inch, which is the width of the tee-slots. The "ears" of the tee are to be 3/32 inch thick. The stock is set in the vice with packing behind, and here "Murphy's Law" immediately takes charge; the available packing plus the 0.370 inch dimension add up to just less than the depth of the vice jaws, but the next size up of packing will be too wide. (This happens so often that it might really be worth machining 1/64 inch off the top of the vice jaws!) So, you may JUST be able to see, in 105b, 25 thou of shimstock set with the packing.

The width of the stock is measured (both ends) and the amount to come off is calculated. This is about 0.059", the stock being slightly undersize. At that depth of cut the cutter can safely work at somewhat more than the regulation

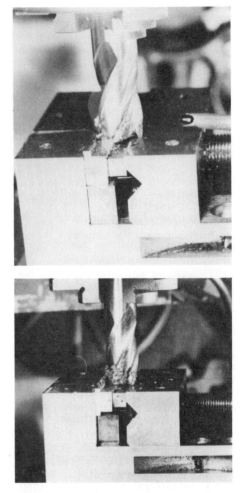

Fig. 105a (top). First stage in making a tee-slot bar.

Fig. 105b. Work reversed to form the opposite edge. See text.

"Quarter of the diameter" as to width. Half inch would do, but I have used $\frac{5}{8}$ inch dia, four flutes. A piece of cigarette paper is stuck to the face of the stock with spit and the cutter brought forward until it

75

whips it off; we will then be within 0.002 inch of the face and careful advance of the work can bring it till it just brushes the surface. Note the reading on the lead-screw handwheel; this is "zero". The vertical slide is then adjusted until the width of the "ear" will be the required 3/32 inch — this is not critical. Lock the vertical slide.

Take the work to the back of the lathe, advance the saddle 0.058 inch and lock it, and take a cut clean across — I used 425 rpm — with a feed-rate of about $3\frac{1}{2}$ inches/minute (Fig. 105a). You will see the coolant feed in the photo, and I used $\frac{3}{4}$ pint on the whole cut about $4\frac{1}{4}$ inch long. Then, without moving anything, remove the work and check the width over the cut with the micrometer. It *should* be to dimension, in which case the workpiece can be reversed, but if not an adjustment may be made to the saddle. WHICH LEADS TO AN IMPORTANT POINT. I *should* have left a small piece of the stock projecting from the vice so that this could be checked *before* removing the stock, so that any correction could be made on a second cut. So, you do that, and I will try to remember next time! The procedure is repeated, (Fig. 105b) and you finish with your tee-bar. Setting up time about 25 minutes, cutting time perhaps two minutes; that is about normal.

A few notes. The stock is, of course, bumped back onto its base with a rawhide mallet. You can check that it is firm by trying to move the packing behind. After that, make a quick check on alignment — bring the work into contact with the cutter and note the leadscrew handwheel index reading, at each end. It should be the same (within the limits of accuracy of the barstock). If it is far out, then your rawhide mallet has shifted the vertical slide! The vice must be tight — use a tommy bar on the handle, and check that the packing is still secure after final tightening. Coolant: I used none on the second side, and you can see how the chips have stuck to the cutter, damp from the previous pass. Finally, the cutter is held in an ordinary 3-jaw, with a total runout of about 2 thou — fair enough in this case, as the thickness and finish on the ears of the Tee are not critical.

LOCOMOTIVE HORNBLOCKS. The above procedure is exactly that used for locomotive hornblocks. The cast GM stick is first squared up (see Fig. 60 page 37) and then, I suggest, cut off to lengths with a slitting saw. Individual blocks can then be machined in pairs, one at each end of the vice jaws, but leave access for the micrometer to measure after each cut. If the hornblocks are fairly thick, take two cuts across in succession so that the cutter is not working at more than half diameter, leaving 5 thou on the thickness to be taken off on a full-width finishing pass. Now, as you have the vertical slide set up you can use it to drill and bore the axle bearings, carefully setting the vertical slide to centre them, and you can then be sure that all holes will be in the same position. It is a long time since I built a loco, but in the days when I did I always left the blocks the odd thou large to the horns, so that they could be properly "fitted".

CROSSHEAD GUIDE SEAT ON CYLINDER COVER, Fig.106. Here we have two faces to machine equidistant from the piston-rod hole. This hole is not large enough to give sufficient size of holding screw, but it can be used for location. A well-fitting peg is screwed into one of the several holes which have been made in my vertical slide over the years and the cover sits on that, but is held down by a normal tee-bolt and clamp. The position of the faces has been marked out and the cover is set square to the base using this marking. Trial cuts are

Fig. 106. Machining
slide-bar seats on a
small cylinder head. A
6-flute cutter is in use.
See text.

made until the marking line JUST shows, when the cutter is traversed over the work using the vertical slide, saddle locked. The clamp is then eased and the casting turned round. NOTE: you must think on, and leave room for a small square between the bolt and the work! At the same setting a cut is taken over the second face. The width is checked by micrometer and if in error (it will be oversize, as we left the marking-out line as a witness) half the error is taken off each face. This procedure ensures both that the faces and the shoulders against

Fig. 106a. Facing a
cylinder block. See
text.

which the ends of the slidebars abut are identically positioned. The cutter in this case has six flutes and rather less helix angle than normal, best for cast GM. It is working almost full face width, but there was only about 35 thou to come off.

FACING A CYLINDER BLOCK, Fig. 106a. This example is a piece of "justified unorthodoxy". The cylinders are for a Stuart compound launch engine, investment moulded, so that the casting needs much less machining allowance, and the "skin" is soft. The cutter used is very old, and though of carbon steel has multiple deep flutes so that despite the necessary low cutting speed the rate of cross-feed can be reasonable. The diameter of the cutter is just sufficient to cover the LP portface. With this setup I am actually taking advantage of the "concavity effect" mentioned on page 33. The work is fed from the front of the lathe to the back and the back of the cutter "interferes" by about 0.00075 inch. So, the roughing is done by the front teeth on the cutter, whilst the face teeth of the cutter, operat-

ing at the back, provide a finishing cut. This is only effective because the face edges of the cutter have been ground very slightly concave, but the effect is to enable a single pass on a rough casting to give an acceptable finish – though of course, the surface had to be dressed to give a face for the valves to slide on.

PORT MILLING, Fig. 107. This is an alternative method of holding a cylinder to that shown in Fig. 64, page 39. I would prefer the latter, as there is less clutter getting in the way of the cutter. This cutter is a straight-flute slot drill, and is held in a 3-jaw chuck. Reprehensible, you may say, for slotting out ports. Not so, for the chuck has clearance on its backplate, and can be set to a runout so small as to be undetectable on a dial indicator. The extension of the plain shank of the cutter, necessary to reach past the clamps, enables the indicator to be used.

There is no need to mark out for the width of the ports, only for the centreline and the lengths – top and bottom in the photos – as we can use the cross-slide

Fig. 107. Milling steam-ports. The clamps in this set-up take up rather too much room.

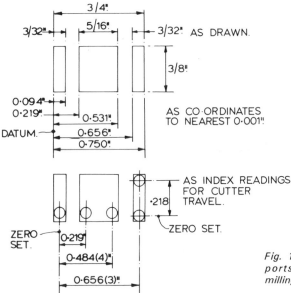

Fig. 108. Setting out steam ports for "co-ordinate" milling.

index and work to co-ordinates. Fig. 108 shows how this is done. Note that the exhaust passage does not matter at all. It can be a round hole if you like, for it plays no part in the timing of the steam events. From the drawing the centres of the two steam ports are derived, as dimensions from the centreline, and the same is done for the lengths of the slots. Set the vertical and cross slides so that the centre of the cutter lies at the intersection of the two centrelines. Then wind the vertical slide down by half the dimension "z" and the cross slide well back and then forward to the index reading corresponding to "x". Plunge in the cutter by half its diameter and (with the cross-slide locked, though this is not really essential with such a light cut) traverse with the vertical slide by the distance "z". Withdraw the cutter, traverse the cross-slide by "x" plus "y", and cut the second port. Note that we have not cut the port full depth, though you

may have to if you cannot follow my next trick. I change the cutter for one slightly less in diameter — the FC3 cutters, far the best for this job, go down by 1/64 inch on diameter at a time — and use this to deepen the two ports. In this way I make sure that successive cuts do not widen the slot. Finally, the exhaust passage is carved out, using either a plain stub drill or a slot drill.

MAKING A SLIDE VALVE. I use exactly the same sort of procedure for making slide valves; you can see the idea, so I will not go into too much detail. Start by machining the back of the valve which carries the valve rod, just bringing it to square or whatever shape it should be, to act as a holding piece. Grip by this in the vice and face the casting to dimension and then machine the sides to width. Use the co-ordinate method to carve out the exhaust cavity — which DOES matter this time — using a small slot-drill if the cavity

is not cast in, Otherwise an end-mill. From this cavity machine the steam edges of the valve. Remove burrs very carefully (on no account bevel the edges) and reverse in the vice to machine the slots for nut and valve rod. This job is done last to reduce the risk of vice pressure crushing the casting.

CONNECTING AND COUPLING RODS. Fig. 109. It is nearly 40 years since I built a locomotive, so I have had to set up and make a rod specially for you – only a small one (it might suit "TICH") but it will show the method. The holes for the crankpin are first drilled and reamed – I do this with the stock held in the vice on the vertical slide and use the co-ordinate method to get the centres right. Two holes are also drilled and tapped in any suitable piece of stock at the same centres. I have a chunk of $\frac{1}{2}$-inch steel which I use for this. In fact, I have several, which over the years have become pepperd with holes suiting the various jobs I have done and might have to be done again. While in the machine, scribe a centre-line corresponding to these holes. I should have said that the rod is, of course, marked out with the various curves, oil-boxes, etc., though most of the work will be dimensioned using the feed-screw indexes. Set the rod on the plate using setscrews, with identical packing washers behind at each end, and then attach the plate to the vertical slide, setting it true with the centreline just mentioned. Fig. 109a shows the setup, with the fluting in progress. This is the "round ended" type of flute; I will deal with the other sort in a moment.

Fig. 109. Making a fluted coupling rod. The work is mounted on a sub-base throughout. a. Fluting with a slot-drill; first operation, with the rod at lathe centre-height. b. Vertical slide adjusted to mill top side of the rod. c. Slide again adjusted to machine the bottom side. d. Showing how the other type of flute can be machined, using a Woodruffe keyway cutter.

Set the work at lathe centreheight, fit a slot drill – I am using a master-slave chuck and an FC3 cutter in the photo – and mill the slot to the full depth in one pass, with the vertical slide locked. The cut is put on using the leadscrew handwheel, but the saddle also is locked whilst the actual cutting is in progress.

Change to an end-mill of diameter suitable for the radii at the ends of the rod where the plain shank runs into the bosses. Rack the vertical slide down by the calculated amount needed to give the correct width and carefully locate the cutter so that it would form the radius at the front end. Note the cross-slide index reading. Repeat for the radius at the other end. Move the vertical slide sufficient for the cutter to clear the work and then reset the cross-slide at the first position. Move the saddle forward to bring the cutter to position – it should be possible to cut full width. Now use the vertical slide to put on cut, but don't go right down (or up, depending how you look at it) for we may need a finishing cut. Leave about 5 thou to come off for this. Feed the cutter along the length of the rod with all save the cross-slide locked. You will almost certainly need coolant, as if the rod gets too hot it may bow. Return and make the finishing cut. This process is seen completed in 109b.

Repeat for the other side. Fig. 109c. This may need two roughing traverses as there is more metal to be removed – for some reason which escapes me I set the work with the oil-boxes below. The outer profiles of these oil-boxes can be formed at the same time, and most of the surplus metal round the bosses can also be removed. You should be able to plunge straight in to do this, as the centre of the end-mill will not be involved. I will deal with the formation of the actual bosses in a moment.

For the alternative type of flute we use a Woodruffe keyway cutter, and this is shown in Fig. 109d. The setup is not quite what I would use, for to save time I employed the same workpiece turned over on the same support plate, just to illustrate it. You can see the snag – there is too much of the support projecting so that the cutter also has to stick out rather a long way. The illustration is self explanatory, I think. The only remark to make is that you do have to choose the cutter diameter rather carefully so that it will not foul the allen screws at the end of the cut. Whether you will need a finishing cut after the first one really depends on how sharp the cutter is; I found just one spot which was a bit rough, so put on another three thou and this cleared it up. The depth of these flutes is not critical so long as they are all very nearly the same.

Note that in Figs. 109b-c-d I would normally use an Autolock chuck to hold the cutter, but this was in use elsewhere at the time. The 3-jaw chuck does make it difficult to see marking-out lines, as well as running a little out of true.

For TAPER RODS the procedure is very similar. In this case you must set three centre lines at one end of the support plate; one the true centre, coinciding with that at the other end, and one each above and below this by half the desired taper. When machining the flute you set the plate first on one of these and then on the other, to make a taper flute. Then do the same for the two outlines, just making sure that you go the right way – set the plate DOWN to do the top face of the rod and vice versa.

END BOSSES. This is a "rounding" operation, and I show in Fig. 110 the method which has been advocated in *Model Engineer* for 50 years or more. I do so with reservations, for it does present some risk. The workpiece is set on a well-fitting

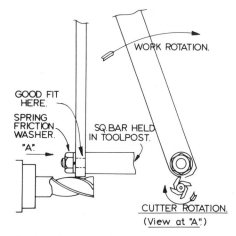

Fig. 110. One method of rounding the end of a rod. See text.

peg on a plate similar to that in 109, and presented to the cylindrical teeth of an endmill. It is then rotated by hand against the direction of rotation of the cutter and the radius formed, taking a little off at a time. The hazard is obvious – if the cutter does happen to "grab" then the work can be damaged and you could possible suffer injury yourself as well. There is the further point that the approach to the blending radius at the end of the circular part is a bit tricky, too, when under manual control – you can never see very well as the cutter gets in the line of sight. Frankly, I find that I can round off the ends of rods just as effectively and in far less time by using a file guided by filing buttons, Where for some reason I do need a machined surface or a really precise radius I set the workpiece up on the faceplate, centred accurately to the hole by clocking a peg or by using the tailstock centre, and present the cutter using the Potts on a vertical slide. The work is then rotated against the cutter by pulling down the belts with the headstock mandrel in back gear. This

gives a steady feed rate and there is no hazard whatever. If you have the worm dividing attachment you can use this as a slow motion drive, and if you own a proper dividing head you can mount the work on this on the saddle and carry the cutter in the headstock. A dividing head does make quite a good slow motion drive!

FORMING A FORKED END. Fig. 111 shows the use of a slitting saw to form a forked end for (e.g.) a valve rod or similar. It also illustrates a problem which many model engineers must face – that of finding their saw has rather a wide pitch tooth. In this case the work is JUST a trifle deeper than the tooth pitch, but the cut would require great care in feeding inwards to avoid grabbing. The work is held in a vice set on the vertical slide, and one way of avoiding the problem is to use the vertical slide to take the feed, bringing the work upwards from below. At the point seen in the photo the risk of "grab" is then almost negligible. The procedure also has the advantage of giving a square bottom to the slot. The alternative method is to use a slot drill, with the work facing the chuck. Note the substantial arbor used by Mr. Broomfield (to whom I am

Fig. 111. Slotting a rod end. A finer pitch cutter would be better. (Photo L. Broomfield).

indebted for the photo) which, carried on a No. 2 M.T. and fitted with a drawbar, will carry the standard 1 inch bore cutters to run dead true.

GANG MILLING. This process is seldom used by model engineers, but as shown in Fig. 112 is very useful when it can be adopted. In this case I had quite a number of small connecting rods to machine. The body has been turned and the large end finished. It is held at that end, with protective shims, in the vice, with the other end supported on a piece of packing which cannot be seen. Two side and face cutters are set on the arbor with a distance-piece between such that the cutters are exactly the right distance apart to machine the other faces of the small end (crosshead end) fork. The two cutters are the same diameter but differ both in width and in the number of teeth, but this does not matter in this application. Their diameter is such that the cut is completed before the workpiece meets the arbor. (This particular vice will not pass below). The operation was very quick, as once the saddle was set at the correct position it was only necessary to grip the work, tap it down onto the packing, and make the cut, one rod after another.

Fig. 112. Gang milling the small end of a connecting rod. A jack supports the work just beneath the cutter.

Fig. 113. Cutting the barring teeth on a small flywheel. The index to the backplate division holes lies behind the chuck.

BARRING RACK ON A FLYWHEEL. Most engines of any size had cast teeth inside the rims of the flywheel for use with a crowbar to turn the engine for maintenance purposes. This (Fig. 113) is a case where the teeth had not been cast in. The wheel is carried in the self-centring chuck and indexed (in this case) from the holes in the backplate – the index pin is out of sight behind. The slot drill is carried in a Potts, which was driven direct from a motor behind the lathe; this, and the belt, has been removed for the photograph. The cutter (5/64 in. dia) is simply plunged in and out again – there is no radial movement at all, as the scale is so small that the absence of a straight side to the barring slot cannot be noticed. A stop to limit saddle traverse is, however, desirable, so that all are the same depth.

SAWING OPERATIONS. Fig. 114 shows a setup by Mr. Derek Beck where a rectangular piece of light alloy is being squared off to length. The saw is carried on a No. 2 MT arbor and drawbar, which can, if need be, have support from the tailstock; not necessary on this occasion. The workpiece is sitting on an "L"-shaped

Fig. 114.
a. (left) Work carried on the cross-slide (Photo Derek Beck).

b. (centre) The MYFORD saw table & clamp (Photo Myford Ltd).

fixture which is, in turn, located by one of the slots in the cross-slide, and is clamped to the short leg of the "L" with a G-cramp. The work is held down by the clamp and tee-bolt seen on the left. To be "proper" the work should be traversed under the cutter from the back of the lathe forwards, but with a narrow cut like this it would not be fatal if the reverse were used.

Fig. 115 illustrates the use of a "SAW TABLE". This is a 65mm Lorch precision screwcutting lathe which is also provied with a hand rest, into which the sawtable can be set. The table must first be aligned

Fig. 115. Cutting off the cap of an eccentric rod freehand. The material is gunmetal, and the saw has fine-pitch teeth.

so that the saw sits in the centre of the slot, and adjusted for height so that as much of the saw projects above as the arbor will permit. The G.M. casting seen was fed by hand, along a marked line and the dimensions of the table permit the cut being taken right across. This method is quick, and provided a good grip and steady feed are maintained, quite safe. The drive belt was set just a little slack so that it would slip in an emergency.

Fig. 116 is another, somewhat unusual application of the sawtable and slitting saw. The application of wooden lagging strips to models of early engines is always a problem – somehow they never look "to scale". In this case I have machined a "tube" of very fine-grained hardwood to slip over the cylinder – cutouts were made later to clear the valve chest etc. This sawtable (Boley-Leinen 50mm watchmaker's lathe) is fitted with an adjustable guide. This was first set so that when the cylinder rested against it the saw lay exactly on the diameter and the table was adjusted to make a cut about 1/64 inch deep. (It is more than that in the photo, as it was about to be used to make the steam chest cutout.) After making a cut at this setting the guide was moved so that the groove engaged on the corner of the guide and held the work in a position which would give the desired spacing of the grooves. As each groove was cut it was engaged with the guide and the next one made. The result is a very evenly spaced set of grooves simulating the individual planks of the full-sized lagging. It is very effective and takes little time. The only important precaution needed is to see that the saw and the guide are accurately aligned – if not dead parallel the grooves will run askew.

EXPANSION LINKS. If there is but a single link required for a Stephenson reverse gear it is probably quicker to use

Fig. 116. Simulating the wooden lagging strips for a steam engine cylinder.

the "drill and file" method, but if two or more are needed then it is worth making a fixture for machining them. Fig. 117 shows one such. It is made of steel gauge plate, but unhardened, 1/8 inch thick. After marking the centreline the three holes shown ringed are drilled and tapped to match the holes for the eccentric rods and lifting link. On this job I had six links, so before tapping these holes I used the tap-drill holes to spot through onto the link blanks. From the centre at the bottom (marked "CL") the correct radius of the slot was struck to a point at the end of the slot marked "Set Rad" and a small hole drilled here with a tiny Slocombe drill. A similar hole was drilled on the centreline in way of the slot – it can just be seen as a dark hole.

The jig can be held on the faceplate of the lathe, cutting to be done with a Potts, or on a small plate on a dividing head on the saddle, cutting done from the lathe mandrel. I generally use the former method. The jigplate is first centred exactly, using the hole marked CL and the tailstock hard centre as a guide, and then clamped up. The mandrel is set in back

Fig. 117. Fixture for slotting and shaping valve-gear expansion links.

gear (or, far better, if you have the head-stock worm dividing gear, use this as a slow motion) and the "set rad" hole brought down to lathe centre-height. A small point centre is set in the Potts and the vertical slide and cross-slide adjusted till this aligns exactly with "Set Rad". Both are then locked. Finally, the necessary travel to cut the length of the slot is established and the teeth on the bull-wheel are marked – or you can use a mark on the faceplate and set up an indicator.

The link blanks are attached in turn (three 7BA screws on this job) and the slot cut with a slot-drill, pulling on the belt to provide a steady feed. I found it necessary to take three cuts – the links were of gauge steel – and as you can see the last cut chewed into the jig; no matter. Once all the links were slotted the cross and vertical slides were reset to machine

the outer profile of the link. The curve for the inner profile was no more than marked out (again, doing all the links at one go) with a spring marking point held in the Potts; the final cutting was done with a file, the bosses being rounded with filing buttons. The slots did need a little refining work, but there was very little metal removed. The die-blocks were, of course, fitted, each to its own slot. As I have said, it is questionable whether such a jig is worth making for a single link – if you wish to machine the slot it is as quick, perhaps, to set it up so that the same procedure can be used "by hand" as it were. But the machining time per link was less than a couple of minutes and for three or more time would certainly be saved. There is the added merit that each link (with its associated dieblock) was interchangeable – holes in identical positions relative to slots of identical radius.

TAP FLUTING. This process seems to be another which, though really quite simple, raises grave apprehension in most model engineers' minds! There is no problem with the division – four flutes, and the world won't come to an end if they are not exactly equally spaced. For general purpose taps Edgar Westbury recommended that the *radius* of the flute be 0.25 × tap diameter, and the final core diameter at the base of the flutes at 0.5 of the tap diameter. This gives a depth of cut from the crest of the threads of *about* 1/7D, or 9/32 of the cutter radius. This gives a very slight hook-shape to the cutting edge. Either of the types of cutter shown in Fig. 70 (page 44) can be used, but both present a small problem in workholding. At the point of the tap the cutter will run very close to the supporting back centre of the dividing engine. The solution is to use the classic "half-centre" here. Indeed, most commercial dividing heads for use on milling machines have not only a half-centre, but the top of the tailstock is machined almost completely away, too. Cutting will be easy enough provided that you realise that you are machining tool-steel and adjust the cutting speed to suit — and use floods of lubricant.

The only serious difficulty is the cleaning up of the teeth of the tap after cutting; there will almost certainly be spelches of metal here. Some practitioners avoid this by fluting before cutting the thread — the threading tool enters the cut on the leading edge of the tap, and any spelch will be on the trailing edges and can be cleaned away without fear of damage. A small finishing cut with the tap centre slightly displaced so that the cutter cuts only on the leading edge of the tap is another alternative. If you have a die of the same thread and its teeth are smaller than the width of the flutes you can, with care, offer this successively down the tap and rotate it on the teeth to clean off any projections, and follow this with a small, very fine file laid along the tap. However, the cutting edges ought to be stoned after hardening anyway (or ground if you have a "Quorn" or similar tool-and-cutter grinder) and this should remove any burrs. Note that burrs on the trailing edge are equally important; if not removed they will distort the thread form. But their removal by filing is easy, as we do not depend on that edge for any cutting.

CONCLUSION. You may well not agree with the methods I have used in these examples, but the joy of this sort of work is contained in the saying "There is no single RIGHT solution to any engineering problem". Your way will very well be the best for you. The experienced worker will complain that all the examples given are easy. I know. That was the idea — everyone has to start somewhere — but wait on, for the next chapter deals with the more elaborate milling operations. I hope that the few examples in this one will give you all an idea or two to work out further in your own way.

CHAPTER 8

Combined Operations and Complex Milling

In this chapter I will deal with operations which either require more complicated set-up, or where special difficulties may arise. I shall deal with gear-cutting, but only rather briefly. The majority of gears made by the amateur are for clocks, and these represent not only a special case, but are also covered more than adequately either in constructional articles or in books. I am indebted to Prof. Dennis Chaddock for some information on profile milling and for some photographs of cam milling operations, both matters of some importance these days. However, though some of the processes may be out of the ordinary, all are, basically, "milling", and there are lessons for all. So, I hope that no reader will be tempted to skip the chapter just because their milling is all "simple"!

ENGINE FRAMES. The alignment of a full-sized engine, whether it be steam or internal combustion, is always a matter of importance. It is equally important for the model engineer, but he is faced with difficulties not met by the full-size engine-erector. The latter may be able to accommodate an error of 5 thou in machining, but even at one inch to the foot this is only four tenths of a thou, and that is close work indeed. So, when machining any engine frame or bedplate it is important to ensure that parallelity and squareness is as close as can be managed, and though dimensional errors can often be corrected in fitting these, too, must be held as close as possible. If the choice has to be made, however, "squareness" must always rank as the most important factor.

Fig. 118 is a photo of a popular model from the Stuart Turner range – their No. 9, with cylinder $1\frac{1}{2}$ inch bore – though this particular model does carry rather a lot of modifications. The design calls for a flat crosshead guide, the main bearings are in square seatings, and there are facings for an optional feed-pump and a governor on the sides. The cylinder is spigoted into a machined facing at the end. The procedure I adopt here is to use the crosshead guide as the reference face, to machine this and the seatings for the main bearings at a single setting, and then face and bore for the cylinder seating as a separate operation, it being easier to "pick up" from the flat crosshead face than to set up to the bore.

Fig. 119 shows the outline drawing of the frame or bed. All dimensions were brought to co-ordinates from the centrelines, and in some cases relative to each other. I don't propose to detail that procedure – it is clear enough; all that is

Fig. 118. A model of a small Fen drainage pumping engine.

needed is care in the arithmetic! Preliminary operations on the casting were to file the underside of the bed so that it could sit without rock, to mark out the main centrelines and centre-pop them in places where they would not be lost in the machining, to prepare a mounting plate, and to drill the four holding-down bolt holes. Fig. 120 shows the plate, but you have seen this before, when milling the connecting rod in Fig. 109. Waste not, want not! This plate was then set up on the vertical slide, held by allen screws. Here I must emphasise that care is needed in siting these. It is all too easy to find that one will foul a casting; where possible I like to have them accessible at all times, but in this case two lay

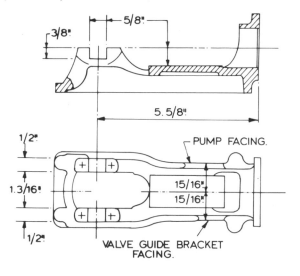

Fig. 119. The bedframe of the engine seen in Fig. 118.

underneath the casting body. Care must be taken at this stage to ensure that the cutters to be used can reach all parts. It is tempting to set the vertical slide in the easiest position, but this is no good if the cross-slide travel won't reach. Similarly, you must take care that the vertical slide can travel sufficiently, both ways. The vertical slide is set dead square by using a dial indicator against the plate, with the bolts tight. This corrects for any taper on the plate – it may only be the odd thou, but that COULD matter.

In Fig. 120a I am setting the casting. The micrometer scribing block (home made) is used, and there is enough clearance in the four holding down bolt holes to permit alignment. (If not, the casting would have to be taken off to move the workplate). This operation is simply to set the casting centreline parallel across the bed; the actual height of the setting does not matter at this stage. Nor does the odd thou matter either, as we shall automatically machine in the true engine centre later. The cutter, seen on the left, is quite small, as it has to get into the corners at the cylinder end, and is held in an Autolock chuck. The projection had to be checked, in case the chuck fouled the cylinder flange, and there was JUST enough clearance. Note the chuck backplate on the mandrel nose. This protects the exposed screw thread, serves as a seating for the chuck damping ring, and is, in addition, painted white on the face to reflect light onto the work. The cut was made by traversing on the cross-slide, with "sideways" movement of the cutter using the vertical slide. Fig. 120b shows machining in progress.

The next step was to retract the saddle and run a cut across the tops of the main bearings, using co-ordinate setting of the leadscrew handwheel to obtain the correct dimension — 121a. The cutter is then changed to a slot-drill and the main bearing slots are cut, Fig. 121b. The setting in this case was done by coordinates for depth, so that the bottom of the slot is accurately positioned relative to the slipper face, but by measurement from the as yet unmachined cylinder seating face, leaving an appropriate machining allowance. This dimension is not critical, and when the face is later machined it can be set accurately from a bar set in the slots.

Fig. 121.a. Facing the tops of the main bearing seats. b. Cutting the slots for the bearing brasses — 2-flute slot-drill.

Fig. 122.a. Setting the casting to lathe centre-height as a reference plane.

The casting is now set accurately with its centreline to lathe centre-height, using my centre-height gauge, Fig. 122a. Using the two "teeth" on the gauge alternately it is possible to work to close limits. An end-mill is then used to machine the cheeks of the main bearings — these locate the crankshaft sideways. The dimensions are, again, determined by co-ordinate setting of the vertical slide index. See Fig. 122b. The seatings on the side of the bed could have been machined in the same way if I had had a "long reach" end mill, but this I had not. However, these are less critical,

Fig. 122.b. Machining the cheeks of the bearing housings, to co-ordinates from the centreline. c. Facing the valve-guide/governor seating. d. Machining the feed-pump mounting face.

so the bed was removed and reset (still on its workplate) on parallels on the cross-slide. Squareness was assured by setting a test-bar in the main bearing slots and clocking this to a mandrel between centres. 121c and d show this work being done. Fig. 123 shows the finished casting

(though with the cylinder face to be machined). There is no detectable error in squareness, and though the slipper face looks as if there is a nasty cutter-mark this is, in fact, a dirt-mark! The surface has, in any case, to be "frosted" with a scraper, if only for better lubrication. The benefits of this procedure were: assured parallelity of the crank to the face of the crosshead slipper: assured centrality of the main bearings to the bed: correct height of the crank above the slipper face: and, believe it or not, both a saving of time and much easier working.

VERTICAL ENGINE STANDARD. This is for a much larger engine – The Stuart No. 1, of 2 inch bore, which can develop more than 1/3 HP. This also has a flat slipper face, but the crosshead guide is slotted. The manufacture was approached in a different way, but still with the slipper face as datum. The main requirement in this (see Fig. 124) is squareness of the two faces relative to the slipper face in both directions. The casting was gripped in the machine vice on the swivelling vertical slide (125a) after marking out the relevant centrelines. The centrelines were set horizontal by tapping the vice on the face of the vertical slide, not by using the swivelling facility. The face of the casting was set true athwart the lathe bed by adjusting the swivelling base and the casting set true in the vertical plane (Fig. 125b) by tapping the casting in the vice jaws – a plastic mallet, of course. These checks were repeated till all was true, and a final check made after the final tightening of the machine vice.

The slipper face was then machined with a shell endmill – Fig. 125c – at one pass, the finish being good enough as it was. The next step was to set the casting truly central to lathe centre-height, using my centre-height gauge as in the previous example. A slot drill was then used to mill

Fig. 123. The finished casting, ready for boring.

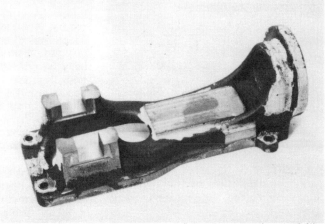

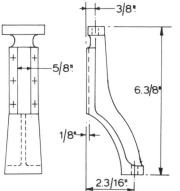

Fig. 124. The standard for a large model vertical steam engine.

Fig. 125a. Steps in setting up the casting. Use of the swivelling vertical slide helps a great deal.

out the crosshead runway. Figs. 126a and b. The cutter was advanced until it just brushed the surface previously machined and the necessary depth of cut established by use of the leadscrew handwheel. Again, a single cut was adequate. It will be noticed that both cutters are held in a 3-jaw self-centring chuck. The Autolock would have been better, but in the operations so far exact dimensional accuracy is not critical; the crosshead slipper has to be fitted to the slot anyway.

93

Fig. 125b. Further steps in setting up the casting.

The end faces now had to be tackled. The top one could have been machined simply by "slabbing" it with a large end-mill, but the other could not have been reached. The vertical slide could have been rotated through 90° and the ends faced, but I was not too happy about the support accorded by the vice to the large overhung base. So, the work was removed from the vice and the vertical slide set squarely as seen in Fig. 126a, with the

Fig. 125c. Facing the slideway surface with a shell end-mill.

94

casting clamped face to the slide. Note the tool-maker's jack supporting the rib against the cutting forces. The lateral squareness of the casting was, of course, checked against the centrelines in the usual way. Machining is being done with a HSS flycutter — actually my ABC boring head. Despite the overhang there was no difficulty and a good finish was obtained at 0.003 inch tooth load. The whole assembly was then turned about to machine the top face, Fig. 126b.

Fig. 125d. Setting the lathe centre-height.

Squareness was checked against the face of the vertical slide, traversed down to the lowest point. This face was machined with a multi-tooth solid mill, which you have seen before. The traverse was all made on the vertical slide. A roughing cut was made, the top-to-base dimension checked with a vernier caliper gauge, and the remainder taken off in one cut. Fig. 127 shows the final result, and the usual

"Inspection Check" revealed no error of squareness, and the top-to-base dimension within 0.001".

THREAD MILLING. This is a process seldom mentioned in model engineering circles, but it has its uses. Fig. 128 shows the dimensions of the spindle of the speed governor for a musical box. It will be seen that the core of the "thread" is only about 50 thou diameter, and the material is carbon tool-steel. Attempts to screwcut this were a failure; sooner or later the piece bent, and attempts to straighten it resulted in either "kinky bits"

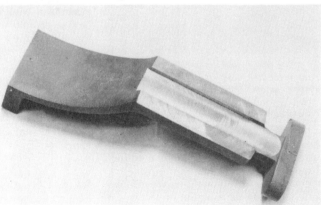

Fig. 126a. Machining the base using the boring head flycutter. Note the jack. b. Facing the top flange.

Fig. 125e. Cutting the crosshead slipper-way with a slot-drill.

Fig. 127. The finished casting.

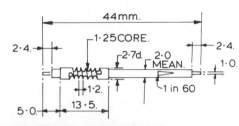

Fig. 128. Sketch of a musical box governor spindle. Dimensions in mm. High-carbon steel.

Fig. 129a. Milling the thread. The vertical slide is set at the helix angle – see text. b. Left: The finished spindle. Right: the original broken part. Centre: A failure – the spindle bent during screwcutting by normal methods.

or outright fracture. So, it was decided to use thread milling. A small clock-gear cutter was available of about the correct shape to form the radii at the root (the original, broken, "worm" was available) but a little too narrow. So, in setting up

(Fig. 129a) the cutter spindle was set at an angle slightly different from the theoretical helix angle of the thread. This caused "interference" which effectively widened the spaces. Checks were made on a brass dummy until the setting was as right as could be expected. The blank had, of course, already been turned, and the work was done on the Lorch precision lathe which had a metric leadscrew. The machining was done with the cutter running rather fast – about 1000 rpm – and using an Extreme Pressure cutting oil, and the thread was formed at a single pass, with a final "shaving" finishing cut. The mandrel was rotated by hand through the back-gear, with care taken to absorb backlash in the screwcutting train. (In fact, on this machine, backlash is almost non-existent when the train is carefully set up). Fig. 129b shows the finished worm assembled with, on the right, the original broken spindle, and in the centre one of the lathe-turned ones snapped off due to overstressing during screw-cutting. On the left is the new mating gear made to replace the original, which had stripped when the failure occurred.

HELICAL FLUTING. This does not crop up very often, even in my workshop, so that I am afraid that I have no photographs to show you. But it is worth a few words, as it can be useful. The technique can be used for helical slots, too, as used in focusing mounts etc. First, however, a little about flutes generally. The method of dividing and the actual cutting is illustrated in Fig. 70a/b, page 44 so I need not elaborate here. The flutes themselves may be of the "architectural" type, Fig. 130a, or with lands, 130b. The difference is made solely by adjustment of the width of the cutter relative to the pitch, the latter being determined by the number of divisions and the circumference of the column. The depth of the flute is very much a matter of taste. In general, those which are cut to a depth equal to the radius of the cutter are rather too bold. I find that a depth about 75% of the radius is about right, but it is advisable to make a few trial cuts on a piece of scrap of the right diameter to be sure. It is worth noting that there may be some problem in the painting if the "Architectural" flute (130a) is used. *Tapered* columns need a little consideration, and as a rule all should be so; better, the lower part—perhaps one third — ought to be parallel and only the top part tapered. If the fluting is carried out ON the taper, then the depth and width of the flute will be constant and the land between will diminish towards the top. If the flute is cut parallel to the axis then the depth and width of the flute will diminish towards the top and the land either remain constant or diminish, depending on the degree of taper. The first condition exaggerates the appearance of the taper, the latter tends to diminish the impression. Clearly, if the flute is cut to a taper between the two extremes the effect will be a "mean". In most cases it is just not worth while and in view of the difficulties involved I usually cut parallel flutes on all columns.

So to the *Helical Flute*. This is, in effect, a screwcutting operation with a very coarse pitch, the "thread" being cut with a milling cutter. It is, however, complicated by the need to "index" for successive flutes. This presents no problems for those

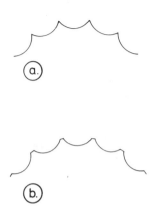

Fig. 130a. "Architectural" fluting.
b. This type of fluting is recommended for painted models.

with "Ornamental Turning Lathes", as a standard accessory is an indexing head on the wheel chain, with which one can cut up to 96-start threads. As an alternative, one of the ornamental chucks can be used set at zero eccentricity — these all have indexing workholders, too. The model engineer's lathe has no such devices (though they can be made, of course). Instead, we index with the changewheels themselves.

Refer to Fig. 84, page 55. Here we were simply using the changewheel train as a plain indexing device and the second wheel is locked. Exactly the same procedure can be used for cutting helices or multi-start threads, but the wheel train will be in motion. When cutting a flute the pitch will, of course, be large so that the wheel on the output stud of the tumbler reverse will be large, engaging with a smaller pinion on the next stud. The train would probably be compound but the procedure is the same as when plain indexing. The train is set up for the desired pitch, bearing in mind that the top wheel must be able to provide the required number of flutes. Thus 60 will give 12, but 90 will not, though it WILL offer 18 which 60 cannot do. This is not a serious problem, as the exact pitch is seldom of importance. This top wheel is then marked as seen in Fig. 84, with the saddle taken back to the starting position of the cut and the clasp-nut engaged. This is important; the marking of the teeth is the *last* operation before cutting takes place, otherwise you may have a lot of idle travel before cutting occurs. Once the marks are on the clasp nut must *not* be disengaged – the saddle is retracted by winding the leadscrew back.

This is the main difference from ordinary screwcutting. The machine CANNOT be power driven – the leadscrew may be making 20 or more revolutions for one of the headstock mandrel. The whole of the driving is done with the leadscrew handwheel. (Except that of the cutting frame or spindle, of course). The first cut is made, usually to full depth less a finishing cut, slowly rotating the leadscrew which in turn rotates the work. When the end of the cut is reached the cutter is stopped and, preferably, withdrawn a trifle, and the saddle retracted to the start again. A small adjustment will be needed to bring the

marks in line, when the change-wheel banjo can be slackened to bring the teeth out of mesh, the first wheel rotated to bring the next mark to that on the second wheel, the teeth re-engaged and the banjo locked up again. The second flute is then cut – and so on. Once all are cut a second light finishing cut can be made. The procedure is simple, but you do need to keep your mind on the job and, of course, take steps to eliminate backlash. I find it sufficient to keep one hand on the lathe chuck.

Now for the type of cutter. This matters more than you might imagine. If you use a ball-ended slot-drill, as in Fig. 70a (page 44) there are no problems at all. For parallel columns the spindle is set vertically, for taper ones (if fluting on the taper) it should be presented horizontally, and that is all. However, when adopting the method of Fig. 70b it is necessary to set the spindle at the helix angle of the flutes, otherwise serious interference will result. Not only will the cut tend to be rather rough, but the flutes will come out wider. See Fig. 131. The angle is quite easily calculated; in the diagram "c" is the circumference of the column $= \pi \times d$. ("d" ought to be at the half-depth of the flute,

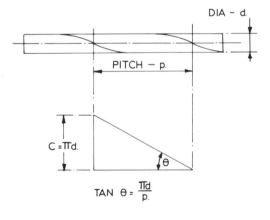

$$\text{TAN } \theta = \frac{\pi d}{p.}$$

Fig. 131. Calculating the angle for cutter setting when machining helical flutes.

but this makes very little difference and can be ignored) "p" is the pitch of the helix, and θ is found by writing

$$\text{Tan } \theta = c/p = \pi d/p$$

The cutting spindle must be set over at this angle —as I had to for thread milling in Fig. 129a. It is by no means critical that the angle be exactly right, but should be as near as possible. If using a Potts mounted as in Fig. 70a it is only necessary to set the spindle over with a protractor on one of the machined faces of the baseplate.

I find that I get equally good finish with either type of cutter — I always take a finishing cut as already explained. The ball-ended slot drill is slower in the cutting, but as there is less setting-up time this makes little difference in the end unless you have a large number of columns to make. One final point, already referred to in earlier chapters. It is important to consider cutter run-though when machining the blank; there must be room for the cutter to clear the workpiece before meeting any workholder.

GEAR CUTTING. Apart from a few minor matters the cutting of gears is quite straightforward, but there is a problem with the cutter itself. First, there are two TYPES of gear teeth; those used in "Engineering" applications and those used for Clock gears. (There are others as well, but we need not bother about them). The "Engineering" gear-tooth is an involute form and the "Horological" gear is cycloidal. The flanks of the teeth are different shapes, and it follows that we need different cutters. I do not propose to go into clock-gear cutting, as this is not only detailed in almost every constructional article, but there are several books available as well — "Clock Wheel

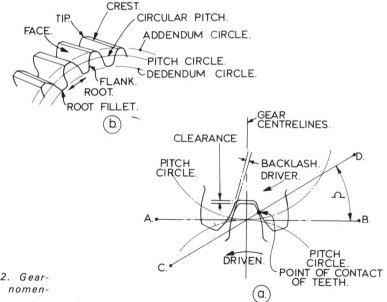

Fig. 132. Gear-tooth nomenclature.

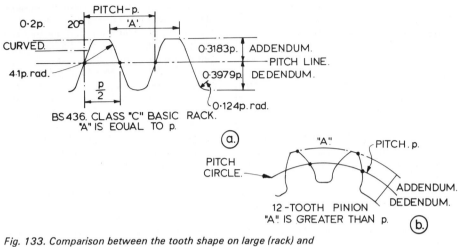

Fig. 133. Comparison between the tooth shape on large (rack) and
small diameter gears of the same tooth standards. This also shows
the proportions of the B.S.436 20° involute tooth.

and Pinion Cutting" by J. Malcolm Wild
(Argus Books) and "Practical Notes on
Wheel-cutting" by Chronos Ltd. See also
"Gear Wheels & Gear Cutting" by A.W.
Marshall (Argus). But the remarks about
the cutters which follow apply equally
well to horological gears.

First, a few definitions. Fig. 132a
shows teeth on two gears in mesh. The
PITCH CIRCLE is an imaginary circle
which will just touch and roll on the pitch
circle of the mating gear when both are
properly engaged. The ADDENDUM is the
height of the tooth above the pitch circle,
and the DEDENDUM is the depth of the
tooth space below the pitch circle. Note
that the addendum and dedendum circles
do not touch; there is a clearance between
the tip of the tooth and the root of the
tooth space, for obvious reasons. The
PITCH of the gear is the distance,
measured *along the circumference* of the
pitch circle, between the corresponding
flanks of adjacent teeth. Note, too, that
there will usually be a slight clearance

between the teeth of the mating gears —
this is the BACKLASH, and is present in
all commercial class gears. (It can be considerable, with no bad effects, on clock
gears). We shall come back to "Pitch" in a
moment. The line "CD" is the "thrust line"
— the line of action of the pressure
between the gear teeth, and the angle Ω
is the PRESSURE ANGLE, measured
against the line "AB", tangential to the
touching pitch circles. This angle is 20°
for gears to BS 436, but $\Omega = 14\frac{1}{2}°$ is
sometimes used in USA. Fig. 132b gives
the names of the parts of the gear tooth,
and is self-explanatory.

Fig. 133a shows the shape of the tooth
of a gear of "infinite" diameter — a rack.
You will see that it has straight flanks,
with a slight relief at the crest; the radius
at the root is there for strength reasons,
and lies within the clearance of Fig. 132a.
*All gears of the same pitch MUST engage
with the same basic rack.* Fig. 132b
shows the tooth shape of a smaller gear.
You will notice that the flanks are curved —

100

as you would expect. Further, the distance "A" on Fig. 133a is equal to the pitch, while the same dimension on 133b is greater – and it is obvious that the smaller the gear the greater this difference becomes. The teeth and, more important, the space between them, differ in gears with different numbers of teeth.

The consequences for anyone wishing to cut a gear are these. *First*, the shape of the cutter will be different for different pressure angles. *Second*, it will be different for involute and cycloidal teeth. (The cycloidal equivalent of 133a shows curves, not straight lines). *Third*, it will be different for different numbers of teeth. The model engineer *may* be able to afford a range of slot-drills covering all likely uses, but the range of cutters needed to cover all pitches and all numbers of teeth is very much greater. Fortunately, for a given pitch, some economy IS possible. It is found that cutters can be designed which will cut a *range* of tooth numbers, and the table below shows the designations.

Cutter No.	1	2	3
No. of teeth	135-up	134-55	54-35

4	5	6	7	8
32-26	25-21	20-17	16-14	13 & 12

A separate cutter is needed for each wheel with less than 12 teeth. Some manufacturers offer "half range" cutters which give less error over the range. Thus cutter No. 3A for 35-44 and 3B for 45-54. The cutter shape will be different, too, according, to the "Class" of gears made, and for "Internal" gears. There is no point in the model engineer using other than "Commercial Class C" standards, as we have not the equipment to work to closer limits.

The PITCH needs some consideration. It is defined as shown in Fig. 132, but this can be inconvenient. If pitch is standardised in "round numbers" – e.g. $\frac{1}{4}$ inch, $\frac{1}{2}$-inch, etc., the pitch circle works out at an awkward figure. Thus a $\frac{1}{4}$ inch pitch wheel of 20 teeth will have a PCD (pitch circle diamter) of 1.591549 inch, and that of a mating 40-tooth wheel is double this. So, the centre distance of the mating pair is 2.387324 . . . inches. Even if we work to the nearest 0.001 inch, this is not an easy figure when setting out centre distances. It is far easier if the centres can be "round numbers" – there is no problem in turning a blank to any micrometer size. Two concepts are used instead of "CIRCULAR PITCH". For inch dimensions we use "DIAMETRAL PITCH" or "DP". This is no more than the number of teeth per inch of diameter. thus a 20t wheel of 10 DP is 2 inch PCD, the 40t wheel is a 4 inch, and the centre-distance is 3 inches.

$$C = \frac{PCD_1 + PCD_2}{2}$$

DP in metric units is a bit awkward, so metric gear teeth (and almost all clock gears) are stated in "MODULES". This is the reciprocal of the DP – the PCD measured in millimetres *divided* by the number of teeth. 10DP (inch) is a module of 2.54. Thus a 20t wheel will have a PCD of 20 × 2.54 = 50.8mm – which is the same 2 inches as before. It is, of course, important to use the correct units of measurement; inches for DP, millimetres, for Module, though CIRCULAR pitch can be measured in either. Now that this country is adopting metric measurements it is prudent not to ASSUME that DP is in inches or M in mm but to say so – DP (Ins) or Module (mm) Circular pitch is. of course, still used especially for teeth of large pitch, and on old machinery will be found on most gears. (Change-wheels for Britannia lathes were, however, in DP even 100 years ago). Pitches are standar-

COMPARISON OF CIRCULAR, DIAMETRAL AND MODULE PITCHES

DP ins	p ins	m mm	DP ins	p ins	m mm	DP ins	p ins	m mm
8	.3927	3.1749	15	.2094	1.6933	25.133	1/8	1.0106
8.378	3/8	3.0318	16	.1963	1.5875	25.4	.1237	1
8.467	.3711	3	16.76	3/16	1.516	26	.1208	.9769
10	.3142	2.54	16.93	.1855	1½	28	.1122	.9071
10.053	5/16	2.5265	18	.1745	1.4111	30	.1047	.8467
10.16	.3092	2.5	20	.1571	1.2700	32	.0982	.7847
12	.2618	2.1166	22	.1428	1.545	34	.0924	.7470
12.566	1/4	2.0212	24	.1309	1.0583	40	.0785	.6350
12.7	.2474	2	25	.1275	1.0160	50	.0628	.5080
14	.2244	1.8143	25.133	1/8	1.0106	50.27	1/16	.5053
						50.8	.0618	1/2

For a complete list of "Engineering" pitches refer to BS436-Machine Cut Gears. For Clock and cycloidal gears see BS 978 part 2.

Note that circular pitch is usually denoted by "p" and the diametral by "P".

dised, and the table above shows the range likely to be needed in model engineering work. Modules for clock gears range from about M.0.2 up to M.1.0 rising by increments of M.0.05.

The use of the DP or Module system does have a further advantage. Oddly enough, it simplifies the calculation of the overall diameter of the blank from which the gear is to be cut. The rule is—

O.D = (t + 2)/DP or = (t + 2) × M.
(t = No. of teeth).

Thus the OD for a 20-tooth gear of 10DP is 22/10 = 2.200 inch and that of a 20 tooth gear of (say) M2.5 is 22 × 2.5 = 55mm. They do not always work out to such easy numbers, but the actual calculation is very easy!

In the same way, the use of the system simplifies the calculation for the depth of cut. This is clearly the sum of the addendum and dedendum (Fig. 132). The former is standardised at 1/P or 1 × M, the latter at 1.157/P or 1.157 × M, so that the depth of cut will be 2.157/P or 2.157 × M. However, there are cases, especially when the pinion has a small number of teeth (less than 18) when this may have to be modified. The "cutting depth" is often marked on the cutter, and it will do no harm to ask the supplier to indicate the design depth when ordering. The "standard depth" automatically provides a root clearance of 0.157/P.

Unfortunately these simple relationships apply only to "Engineering" (including model engineering) gears of 20° involute form. Those for clock gears and any other applications of cycloidal teeth (fortunately rare) follow the same principle, but the constants are different. Clock gears are complicated, too, by the fact that the constants are different for wheels and pinions, and in some cases for different pitches. Suppliers of cutters usually issue charts for use with their tools, and tables are also given in "Clock Wheel and Pinion Cutting" by J. Malcolm Wild (Argus Books Ltd). Care has to be taken when restoring *old* clocks, and it is only prudent to copy the depth of tooth and, where the evidence remains, blank diameter, from the original. Few clocks over 100 years old will have teeth to current standards anyway.

There is one more factor which has to be considered – that of the physical size of the cutter. In industry even cutters for quite small pitches (large DP numbers) will have a bore for the arbor no smaller than 1 inch. On the other hand, clock gears may have metric bores, 6mm being common. Clearly, even if an arbor can be made to carry a 1 inch bore cutter the O.D. may use up all the available space on the machine, while a cutter of small bore may result in the arbor being too slender. When enquiring for a particular gear-cutter it is advisable to specify alternative bores and the limit on the overall diameter which can be accommodated.

In *ordering* a cutter it is, from what has gone before, necessary to specify:

● Pitch, and remember to state metric or imperial.
● Number of teeth in the wheel being cut.
● The standard tooth form – e.g. BS346 Class C,
      or the relevant clock gear standard.
● Bore of the cutter
● Maximum and minimum cutter O.D. which can be accepted
● Material – HSS or Carbon Tool-steel.
● If the Pinion (the smaller wheel) has less than 18 teeth, the number of teeth in the mating gear. This will ensure that the right "correction" is made on the cutter. (This is automatic on most clock pinion cutters).

In the case of clock gears, especially when required for cutting replacements for an old clock, it may be necessary to examine the old wheel to ascertain whether the root has square corners or rounded, but as I have said, clock gear cutting can be rather special and those concerned are strongly recommended to acquire a specialist book on the subject.

GEARCUTTING PROCEDURE. This is no different from any other milling process which involves dividing. The alternatives available are to mount the cutter on the machine arbor and the work on a dividing engine on the saddle, or vice versa. There are two factors governing the choice. First, the availability of a convenient dividing device. Watchmakers' lathes often have all the dividing circles needed for most standard clock gears available on the mandrel pulley, and it is then just as simple to set up a milling spindle on the saddle as it would be to set up a dividing head. On the other hand, a Potts spindle – or even one of the more substantial types – would not be man enough to cut a set of change wheels in cast iron. For such an application the availability of the back-gear would make it preferable, if not essential, to carry the cutter on the lathe mandrel. Fig. 134 shows a gear being cut on a Myford lathe in this fashion, while Fig. 135 shows a milling spindle on the saddle cutting a clock gear using a division plate on the mandrel.

The normal requirements of squareness and correct setting to centrelines are rather more important when gear cutting. But this IS no more than taking care and checking everything twice. Any error here will result in a tooth profile of the wrong shape. It is particularly important that the centre of the cutter should lie exactly above the centreline of the wheel being cut. All reputable cutters will have the cutting profile central to the flat faces and these can be used for setting up, Fig. 136. It is also important to cut to the correct depth, and this means that the setting of the zero of the infeed is important. Once all is set up the cutter can be brought down very slowly to the wheel blank, on which a piece of cigarette paper* has been set. As soon as this is whipped off by the cutter a very small further movement will cause a very slight mark to appear on the wheel, and the zero can then be set.

Even small wheels in brass will benefit from a finishing cut, and any wheel of any size should be given a series of moderate successive cuts. The setup is inherently "whippy" and there is always risk of chatter if too much is taken off at one cut. Once chatter develops it may be very difficult to get rid of it. Naturally, sharp

*Cigarette paper is sold by tobacconists as "RIZLA" paper. "Red packet" is 0.001 in. thick, "Green Packet" about 0.0015 in.

cutters will help, and as most are form relieved this should present no problem, for even if you have no cutter grinder a rub with a slip-stone over the front face (never the profiled sides) will improve matters. One final point – always mark the tooth at which cutting starts. It is all too easy when making the finishing cut to "leave the last one out"!

There are two points which will bear mentioning. First, the cutter cuts the *space*, and forms the tooth as a consequence. If there is to be a tolerance on depth of cut the cut should be too deep rather than too shallow. A deep cut will (within reason) give teeth of the right form, but there will be a bit more backlash. Second, there are some who hold that if the O.D. of the blank is made oversize the gears will "mesh better". This is nonsense, even if the depth of cut is increased to compensate. The effect, if the depth of cut is not altered, is to make the

Fig. 134. Gear-cutting with the dividing head on the saddle. Note the use of the swivelling slide to cope with the large wheel. (Photo Myford Ltd).

Fig. 135. Gear-cutting with the cutter on the saddle, dividing from the lathe mandrel. (Photo J.M. Wild).

effective pitch circle larger, and this will lead to poor operation. If the depth of cut IS altered to give the correct pitch circle all that happens is that the crest of the tooth takes up more of the root clearance in the mating gear. There *are* situations where the O.D. of the blank can be reduced with advantage, *provided* that the depth of cut is corrected, but they are rare and rather special. A blank which is accidentally machined oversize should be reduced, but one which is somewhat undersize can be used safely if the depth of cut is adjusted.

FLYCUTTERS. Flycutters are often used for clock-gears and most contributors of such articles descibe how they can be made. Can they be used for making

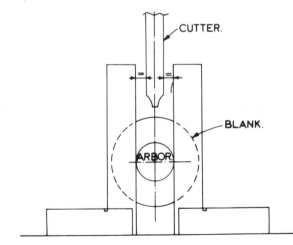

Fig. 136. Centring the cutter. The squares can be set against either the blank or the mandrel. It is, of course, prudent to check that the cutter teeth are central to the side faces.

105

"engineering" gears? For brass, yes, and possibly for light alloy or Tufnol (which is an excellent gear material, by the way) but I would hate to have to machine a steel or cast iron gear with one. However, the problem is not so much the cutting as the making. To work together properly gear teeth must be of the correct shape, and though there are ways of generating a *circular arc* profile this is no more than an approximation to the involute form. For pitches smaller than 3/16 inch (16DP or M. 1.5) such circular flanks may have to be tolerated, but on the only occasion on which I have made a flycutter for BS436 type gear form I filed up the cutter using a gear wheel of almost the same size as that which I wished to cut. For those wishing to make cutters there is an excellent article by Mr. D.J. Unwin in *Model Engineer,* 1st October and 15th October 1971, starting at page 966. The same article also includes some helpful details on setting up and cutting. Small (i.e. Model Engineering and Horological) gear-cutters are nowadays a lot cheaper than they were, and if any quantity of gears of the same pitch and comparable tooth count are to be cut it is not too expensive to buy the proper form-relieved cutters. They will last a long time.

I hesitate to mention this, but in the old days most "cut" gears of any size were done by hand! All the gears in the screw-cutting train of an old lathe I have were marked out and then filed out, as were those on an 18th century church clock which I restored some time ago. The first has served for 180 years, the latter is still keeping time after 250!

CAM MILLING. The making of cams is critical to any attempt to model I.C. engines, and I often suspect that it is this part of the manufacture that discourages many model makers from attempting one. In fact, it is not too difficult; the actual machining is fairly simple, but the preparatory work does include some rather careful work on the drawing board. Fig. 137a shows a typical cam profile and it is readily seen that the actual "cam" part is a hump rising from a "base circle." At "b" the cam is rotated by angle AOB from the horizontal so that a horizontal plane "pp" lies just on the base circle. If a milling cutter were run across this would produce a flat. At "c" the cam has been rotated further, and we have the plane "pp" distance "x" from the base circle. Again, a cutter could be traversed to make a flat. Again at "d", where the flat distance "y" from the base circle and then at "e" again, the flat distant "z" this time. The resulting workpiece would be as at "f", shown to larger scale. Not much of a cam, but if we carry this out at close enough intervals of angle AOB the cam profile will be a series of tiny flats, each very accurately dimensioned, with only tiny ridges in between to clean up. Naturally, to produce the circular part we need only rotate the work using the dividing device as a driver, and the flat face cutter (fly-cutter or slot-drill) will produce a perfect cylinder.

That is the basis of the method. The cam is drawn out as large as possible, perhaps ten or twenty times full size. A series of radial lines is drawn at close, regular, intervals. These intervals can either be (say) 5 or even 3 degrees, or could be the intervals on, say, a 96 or 100-hole dividing disc (the 120 disc would give intervals of 3°). The "flat" is drawn at right angles to the radial lines so that it is just tangential to the cam profile. See Fig. 138. Note that these tangential lines may touch the cam profile at a point far removed from the radial line itself. Only two of these sets of lines are drawn in Fig 138, for clarity, but there will be a fair maze when all are there. Even though it is necessary to draw them only on half

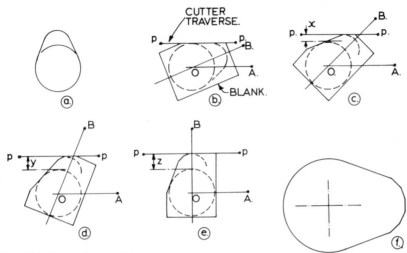

Fig. 137. Steps in machining a cam profile. See text.

the cam if it is symmetrical you do have to be very careful to avoid confusion!

The first radial is Oa and the "flat" line is cb, b being the point of tangent. The second is Op, the flat being rq. If you now measure the radial distances from c and q to the base circle, indicated as x and y, these are (when corrected for the scale of the drawing) the "lift" of the cutter needed from the base circle to cut that

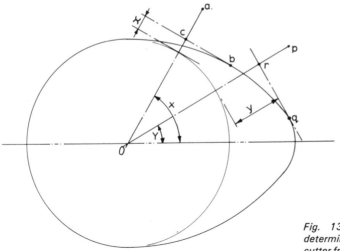

Fig. 138. Construction for determining the offset of the cutter from the base circle.

Fig. 139. Machining a double cam for a "KIWI" petrol engine. (Photo D.H. Chaddock).

part of the cam profile. These ordinates are then tabulated against the angles (or number of holes) "X", "Y" etc. It is at this stage that errors creep in; the drawing can be misread and an ordinate is easily missed. The table should be checked over several times.

As in the case of gear-cutter it is a matter of choice whether you carry the cutter from the headstock or on a milling spindle – in which connection I would call your attention to the wooden pulley in the photo. This, attached to a flange instead of the normal pulley, gives plenty of grip at a lower speed.

This photo, Fig. 139, is the setup used by Prof. Dennis Chaddock a good many years ago to machine the cams for Edgar Westbury's "Kiwi", an O.H.V. pushrod petrol engine. His milling spindle is improvised and he is using changewheels for the dividing – no elaborate equipment at all. The flycutter is home-made, the advantage being that it can be made very sharp, and also, having a single point, is bound to generate a flat surface (providing

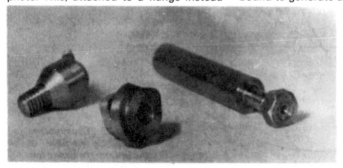

Fig. 140. Left. The flycutter used in Fig. 139. Centre. A part-machined cam. Right. The workholding arbor. (Photo D.H. Chaddock).

the two axes are at right-angles). Fig. 140 shows the cutter, the cam arbor, and a part-machined cam – you will see that both inlet and exhaust cams are in one piece. The blank is simply reversed on the mandrel to cut the opposite profile; the keyway seen in the photo looking after the phasing.

For similar purposes I use slot-drills, fed in sideways. I am reasonably sure that the two cutting edges are in line – this can easily be checked – and they have the advantage that they can be plunged in radially for roughing out. However, for this type of cam the cutter will quite happily work full depth – the lift on a model cam looks a good deal larger than it actually is. It is, of course, desirable (sometimes important) that the centre line of the cutter be coincident and at right-angles to that of the workpiece.

One final point. Tick off each entry on the index sheet as you machine it, otherwise you may miss one – or do the same one twice!

PROFILE MILLING. It is usually difficult to machine to marked out lines when milling; it is often a job to see them without losing some hair on the spindle, and even sharp cutters sometimes raise a spelch of metal at the cut edge. If more than one item is to be machined to the same shape it is often worth while making a template to guide the cutter. I am again indebted to Prof. Chaddock for Fig. 141 – again taken many years ago – where he is machining the endplates for a model of a Zoller supercharger. This called for a number of radial ribs — you can see a finished endplate on the left – springing from the bearing boss, which is eccentric to the centre of the plate. It would be very difficult to get these right by marking off and working to a line, the more so as those on each end should be identical. Using a template to control the cutter gets

Fig. 141. Using a template to machine the ribs on the endplate of a model ZOLLER supercharger. (Photo D.H. Chaddock).

over this very nicely. You can see this attached to the workpiece by cheese-head screws, which also serve to hold the work to a thick underbase – attached, in turn, to the lathe cross-slide.

The cutter is home-made and is necked down just above the relatively short cutting flutes. (Fig 142). This necked down part rubs against the template which must, of course, be shaped to compensate for the difference in diameter of cutter and rubber. By working on the two traverses, cross-slide and saddle, the greater part of the unwanted metal can be chewed out quickly. There is no risk of overshooting as the template will stop it. Finally, the profile can be cut accurately by working the traverses close to the template. As can be seen from the finished endplate, straight ribs *are* straight and the circular arcs truly circular. This is a procedure which has a number of applications; it is simply a matter of choice whether to go to the trouble of making a template or to devise a perhaps even more complicated set-up on a rotary table – assuming that you have one. The equipment used by Prof. Chaddock is that illustrated in Fig. 76, page 49 which will make it clear that no elaborate milling equipment is needed. As the template controls the limit of all cuts the lack of rigidity of the set-up and the dubious accuracy of a drill-chuck to hold the cutter doesn't matter. The arrangement can equally well be used with the cutter held in the headstock mandrel and the work mounted on a vertical slide.

CONCLUSION. This chapter is not really intended to show you how processes *ought* to be done, but rather how they can and have been done, so that you can develop your own ideas accordingly. I hope that I have shown that even the most complex process is, basically, no more than a sum of simple ideas, and that you will not, in future, be discouraged when faced with an apparently impossible milling job!

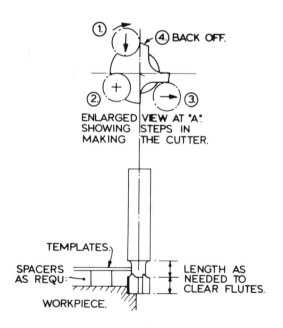

ENLARGED VIEW AT "A".
SHOWING STEPS IN
MAKING THE CUTTER.

Fig. 142. Setup of cutter and template – packing thickness exaggerated for clarity. Top shows a suggested method of making the special cutter.

CHAPTER 9

Care of Cutters

Before dealing with the care and resharpening of cutters it may be advisable to have a few words about their manufacture. I do not propose to go into this in great detail, as the main reason for making one these days is that there is no standard cutter available, so that every, or almost every, home-made cutter will be a "special". The most usual requirement is for an odd diameter of slot-drill, and the design is almost standardised at Fig. 143a. This is a pity, for it will not work AS a slot-drill; the sawcut at the centreline means that when plunged straight down there will be a pip of uncut metal on that centreline. It will work well as an endmill,

of course, and if used to clean up the profile of a cored-out steam port will give satisfactory results. The preferred arrangement is at 143b, with one of the end cutter blades reaching just past the centreline. It is now a true slot-drill and will, of course, perform as an endmill as well.

The cutting edges should be backed off at about 30° but leaving a "witness" between 1/32 and 1/64 inch wide. This is stoned to the cutting angle after hardening. The cutting rake on the side-flutes will, of course, be very slightly negative as the "front" edge is not on the centre-line. But if the thickness of the blades is made not more than 1/4 of the diameter the

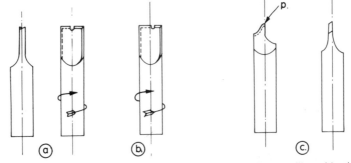

Fig. 143a. "Classical" home-made slot-drill. b. Offsetting the flutes will enable the cutter to "plunge". c. A single-sided profiling cutter. The cutting edge can now be on the true centreline.

effect will be negligible. Negative rake on the cylindrical cutting edge can be avoided by using a single-sided cutter — Fig. 143c. Such cutters are universal in ornamental turning, and they are particularly useful when profiling is required. In this case the blade is filed or milled to the centreline. There is no reason why the point, "p", should not be set just a trifle beyond the axis of the cutter.

Given means of dividing and a cutter there is no reason why the more conventional type of milling cutter cannot be made. To be frank, the problem is not so much the machining of the blank (see figs 38 and 142) or even the sharpening after hardening, as difficulties in the heat treatment. Fluting with an endmill would present few problems provided that the fluting cutter were treated with an oilstone to round off the corners — a sharp corner at the root of the flute is just asking for it to crack — but cutters of any size do present difficulties. To get over this for cutters which ARE special, and which will, therefore, have little use, it is probably worth while considering casehardening. If the steel is well annealed before machining distortion should not then be a problem, and if four or five treatments with Kasenit are given the case will be thick enough to take light stoning to sharpen. As a bonus the cutting edge will be much harder than silver steel, as it does not need tempering.

The problem with cutters of any size is that unless you have a furnace you cannot keep the work up to temperature long enough, and owing to its size and heat capacity the quench will not be as thorough as with smaller cutters. However, if circumstances demand such a cutter, bring up to heat very slowly, and hold the top temperature (780-790°C for silver steel) for as near as you can manage for one hour per inch of diameter. This may cause

scaling, so either cover the work with thick paste of powdered chalk and water or, better, heat it in a box filled with lime to which 10% of charcoal has been added. Quench in brine (1lb. salt per gallon of water) at about 70°F, using enough agitation to detach steam bubbles, NOT a violent one, with a combined up-and-down and round-and-round motion. Take from the brine when all "fizzing" has stopped and immediately repeat in fresh clean water. Do not attempt to temper "by colour". You are unlikely to get it right (what SORT of straw?) and again, the tempering should last for an hour per inch, too. Use the domestic oven, which has a thermostat, and set this at 230°C — cook it for as long as you please. I think you will find that temperature is right for scones! (Small cutters can be tempered for work on brass in the chip-pan). You will find more details of heat treatment in Argus Books' "Hardening, Tempering and Heat Treatment". Those who have a "Quorn" tool-and-cutter grinder can, of course, chew a small milling cutter from ready hardened high-speed steel; broken Slocombe drills are very useful! But a properly hardened and tempered carbon steel is, in fact, harder than HSS and provided you keep it cool by reducing the cutting speed will both cut better and give a better finish in many cases.

CUTTER STORAGE. More cutters are blunted by bad storage than in use if they are just "kept in a drawer". Many, indeed, are blunted before you get them — see them tipped out in bins at "bargain counters" at exhibitions! Proper storage costs little, far less than the cost of the tools themselves. For shank-type cutters — endmills, slotdrills, etc, — I use two methods. Some are kept in a drawer furnished with a base-block bored with a series of holes slightly larger than the shanks. This block is well impregnated with oil and the business ends of the cutters are all oiled after cleaning before putting them away. The second method uses the white expanded polystyrene block material much used as packing these days. This can be cut to sit in the base of a drawer or box with a hot knife. Grooves are then made to suit the cutters by heating a piece of round M.S. and pressing it into the surface. It needs very little heat – a "spit just fizzes" temperature is enough. The choice between this method and the "holes" depends on no more than how deep is the drawer – some are too shallow to accept cutters standing on end. Slitting saws are kept in a drawer on wooden pegs let into the base, far enough apart to ensure that they do not touch, and some people do the same on a board or inside a cupboard door. I use the same method for side-and-face or gear-cutters, too. Nothing elaborate at all, but it does make a big difference to the cutting edges. One point – if you are fortunate enough to be able to keep separate cutters for brass, do so. In the common sizes – perhaps half a dozen or so – I keep new cutters for brass etc before using them on steel, with a yellow paint-dab to remind me. By the time the paint is worn off the cutter usually has lost its pristine edge and can be used on steel or cast iron. My carbon steel cutters all have a band of blue paint round the shank.

CUTTER SHARPENING. I have already mentioned that the weakest part of the usual endmill is the corner. As soon as this becomes even slightly rounded it will rub. If you consider the cutting action again, mentioned in Chapter 2, you will realise that as the tooth first meets the metal the chip thickness is very small indeed. If the tooth corner is slightly rounded then it will not "enter" – it will rub until the pressure becomes sufficient to force it into the workpiece. This will be

quite sudden and the shock causes the vibration so often found when milling. In addition, the cutter will spring sideways, which means that the tooth on the opposite side, which *is* cutting properly, will spring out a little, giving a ridged finish. So, in all cases where a sharp corner at the bottom of the cut is not an essential part of the operation, the first expedient to use is to stone, very lightly, this sharp corner. (Naturally, if the cutter is required only for surfacing, you can put a deliberate bevel here, with great advantage both to cutter life and to finish).

There is little difficulty in tuning up the end-teeth of an endmill. This can be done with a fine India oilstone, using a thin oil – Tellus II or "Three-in-One". I use what is called a "Tool-maker's Taper" or "Machinist's Stone" – a double-ended taper, fine grade India. This enables one to get at cutter teeth without touching the business edge of the next one. You must do your best to keep to the original angle, noting that there are two – see Fig. 144. There is no need to stone at "a". However, once the land at "b" has been stoned or sharpened several times it will become too wide, and at this stage it is desirable to have the larger relief surface "a" reground. It is very difficult to hone the front (rake) face of a helical cutter, but if it has straight teeth then a light rub here will be advantageous.

Retouching the teeth on the cylinder of

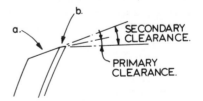

Fig. 144. The secondary clearance at "a" must be ground when stoning of the primary clearance at "b" results in too wide a land. See text.

113

Fig. 145. The "QUORN" Universal tool and cutter grinder. (Photo Model Engineering Services).

the cutter is not at all easy. Remember that ANY sharpening here will alter the diameter of the cutter, and this may be serious with a slot-drill. Fortunately the chief "bluntness" is usually found at the corner and if this is corrected the cutter will behave again. Side-and-face cutters present no difficulty, and the straight tooth face cutter – Fig. 16 – can be touched up without difficulty. Gear cutters, and any other form-relieved type, should, of course, be stoned up ONLY on the face. Any attempt to sharpen the profile will destroy the shape.

CUTTER GRINDING. The whole face of milling by model engineers has been changed in the last few years by the introduction. of home-made tool and cutter grinders. It is now possible for those able to build such a machine to maintain their cutters to a standard equal to that found in any industrial toolroom. The implications are rather deeper than many imagine. Anyone having these facilities can use their cutters at "industrial" rates, knowing that though this inevitably shortens the life of the cutting edge this edge can easily be restored. The cutting speeds and feedrates given on page 26. assume that preservation of the cutter is more important than rate of metal removal. For the benefit of those who have made themselves a cutter-grinder I give the recommended rates for INDUSTRIAL conditions in App. I by courtesy of Messrs Clarkson International PLC. You may care to compare these, and make up your mind whether it is worth building a grinder!

The Quorn was the first to be introduced, and castings are available from Model Engineering Services Ltd, 6 Kennet Vale, Brockwell, Chesterfield. This, shown in fig. 145, is a truly "universal" machine and will sharpen almost anything. It can, as I have already suggested, be used actually for the manufacture of cutters from ready-hardened HSS blanks. This is more important than is often realised, for it means that distortion in hardening is completely avoided. Oddly enough, more people are put off by the number of ball handles seen in the photo than from any fear of other machining operations involved in its

making! This need not worry you – most of those seldom needed can be replaced by socket-screws with very little disadvantage in using the machine. To go into the details of cutter grinding in this book would make it far too long, but there is no need, for the designer of the Quorn, Prof. D.H. Chaddock, has written a book covering both manufacture and use (The 'Quorn' Tool and Cutter Grinder" – Argus Books Ltd). This even covers thread grinding.

A less elaborate cutter grinder is the Kennet, Fig. 146, also available as a castings set from Model Engineering Services Ltd. This machine is deliberately limited in its applications, so that both manufacture and use is simplified as far as is possible. It can sharpen lathe tools, slot drills, endmills, slitting saws and any fairly narrow straight tooth face mills, but not side-and face cutters or the flutes of endmills. Nevertheless it does meet the

Fig. 146. The "KENNET" tool and cutter grinder. (Photo Model Engineering Services).

needs of those whose range of cutters is relatively small but who find milling an essential part of their work.

Offhand Grinding "All the rules" say that you should never try to grind a milling cutter with the ordinary double-ended bench grinder. Despite that I used no other method for 30 years, and provided great care is taken and the wheel is kept well surfaced cutters can be restored, and will certainly be better than a blunt one − a lot better. A secure tool-rest is needed, and if yours has a silly sheet-metal thing attached to the wheel guard, bolt down the machine and build up a proper rest, set on the bench. It is essential that the tool support be solid − and that applies to ALL offhand grinding, despite the name. A small vee-block can be set on the rest at a height such that the tangential angle of the wheel (always use the circumference, not the side) is correct for the cutter to be ground. The cutter axis must be square to the wheel. Then the only problem is to grind no more off any one end tooth than from any others. I deal with this by taking a slight "cut" from each tooth in turn. You get used to the sound, and, using the finer of the two wheels, very often two cuts round the tool will give a good edge. The same principle can be used for bevelling the corners of endmills.

The limitations are − you cannot grind the cylinder flute; it is difficult, if not impossible, to grind the end teeth of cutters with more than four flutes; no attempt should be made to grind profiled cutters − ball ended slot drills, for example; and though slitting saws CAN be ground it is impossible to preserve their circularity unless a special rig is made. So, the common tool-grinder has but limited use, but it is worth remembering that even a hand-sharpened endmill or slot drill is better than a blunt one!

APPENDICES

Appendix I
SPEEDS AND FEEDS FOR "CLARKSON" STANDARD ENDMILLS AND SLOT DRILLS

Note. These figures relate to cutters used in *industrial* conditions, with resharpening as soon as distress is evident, and when used in milling machines. Some reduction is necessary for use in a lathe, and page 27 should be consulted for cutters when long life is of greater importance than rate of metal removal.

STANDARD END MILLS

Dia Inches	Tough Steel 56 Ton UTS		Med. Steel 40 Ton UTS		Cast Iron, P.B.		Mild Steel 30 Ton UTS		Brass and Aluminium	
	RPM	Feed, Ins/min	RPM	Feed, Ins/min	RPM	Feed, Ins/min	RPM	Feed, Ins/min	RPM	Feed, Ins/min
1/8	1100	3/8	2445	15/16	1920	1	3210	1 1/4	8100	4
3/16	720	5/8	1635	1 5/8	1280	1 7/16	2140	2 1/8	5350	5 1/2
1/4	540	7/8	1223	1 15/16	960	1 3/4	1600	3 1/4	4000	8
5/16	430	1 1/16	980	2 15/16	770	2 1/2	1280	4 1/8	3200	11
3/8	360	1 3/16	817	3 1/4	640	2 5/8	1070	4 1/4	2700	11
1/2	270	1 15/16	612	3 7/8	480	3	800	5 1/16	2000	13
5/8	210	1 3/8	490	3 7/8	385	3 1/8	642	5 1/8	1600	13
3/4	180	1 1/2	410	4 1/16	320	3 1/2	535	5 5/16	1350	14
7/8	155	1 3/4	350	4 1/4	275	3 3/8	458	5 1/2	1145	14
1	135	1 5/8	306	3 5/8	240	2 7/8	400	4 13/16	1000	12

STANDARD SLOT DRILLS

Dia Inches	Tough Steel 56 Ton UTS		Med. Steel 40 Ton UTS		Cast Iron, P.B.		Mild Steel 30 Ton UTS		Brass and Aluminium	
	RPM	Feed, Ins/min	RPM	Feed, Ins/min	RPM	Feed, Ins/min	RPM	Feed, Ins/min	RPM	Feed, Ins/min
1/8	1225	1/2	2445	1 5/16	2140	1 1/8	3210	1 5/8	9170	4 1/2
3/16	820	3/4	1634	1 5/16	1430	1 1/2	2140	2 1/8	6110	6
1/4	610	1	1223	2 5/16	1070	2	1605	3.1/16	4590	6
5/16	490	1 1/4	978	2 15/16	855	2 3/4	1283	4 1/8	3665	12
3/8	410	1 1/4	817	2 15/16	715	2 3/4	1070	4 1/8	3055	12
7/16	350	1 1/2	700	3 5/8	610	3	916	4 9/16	2625	13
1/2	310	1 1/2	612	4	535	3 1/2	800	5 1/4	2295	15
5/8	245	1 1/2	489	3 7/8	430	3 1/8	642	5 1/4	1835	15
3/4	200	1 1/4	409	3 1/4	360	2 7/8	535	4 1/4	1525	12
7/8	175	1 1/8	350	2 7/8	305	2 1/2	458	3 5/8	1315	10 1/2
1	150	1	306	2 7/16	265	2 1/8	400	3 1/4	1145	9 1/2

See page 27 for the recommended depths and widths of cut for endmills and slotdrills.

Appendix II
INDEXING WITH CHANGE-WHEELS

No.	Wheels	No.	Wheels
2	Any Even No.	41	NONE
3	60, 45, 30	42	NONE
4	60, 40, 80	43	(43)
5	60, 50, 40	44	(44)
		45	45, (90)
6	60, 30, (90)		
7	70, 35, (21)	46	(46)
8	40, (80)	47	(47)
9	45, (81)	48	(48)
10	60, 50, 40	49	NONE
		50	50, (100)
11	55		
12	60	51	(51)
13	65	52	(52)
14	70	53	(53)
15	60, 75, 45	54	NONE
		55	55
16	(64) (80) (48)		
17	(51)	Indexable Nos	
18	(90)	only are shown	
19	38	below	
20	60, 40, 20	59	(59)
		60	60
21	(63)* (21)*		
22	(44)	62	(62)
23	(46)	63	(63)*
24	(48)	64	(64)
25	50, 75, 25	65	65
26	(52)	70	70
27	(27)	73	(73)
28	(28)	75	75
29	NONE	80	(80)
30	60, 30, (90)	81	(81)
36	NONE	85	(85)
37	NONE	90	(90)
38	38	95	(95)
39	(39)	100	(100)
40	40, 80	127	(127)*

Wheels shown in brackets are additional
to the standard set, but available at extra
cost. Wheels marked * are used in the
normal metric chain.

HOLES AVAILABLE IN COMMERCIAL DIVISION PLATES

MYFORD
Standard No. 1 91, 77, 49, 38, 34, 32
          No. 2 47, 46, 43, 42, 41, 37, 31, 29
Extra   No. 3 97, 83, 73, 67, 61, 27
Extra   No. 4 89, 79, 71, 66, 59, 53

CHRONOS

DD.61	100, 96, 84, 80, 78, 72, 64, 62, 60, 59
DD.62	120, 100, 96, 90, 84, 80, 78, 72, 64, 62
DD.63	88, 75, 70, 63, 59, 56, 54, 49, 41, 34
DD.64	12, 10, 9, 8, 7, 6
DD.65	144, 120, 114, 112, 100, 96, 84, 70
DD.66	144, 132, 118, 114, 112, 108, 98, 74, 70, 58.

Plates DD. 65R and DD.65S carry additional rows of 90 and 49 holes respectively compared with DD.65.

BROWN & SHARPE (For use with 40/1 worm dividing head)

No. 1	15, 16, 17, 18, 19, 20
No. 2	21, 23, 27, 29, 31, 33
No. 3	37, 39, 41, 43, 47, 49

Some models have the same numbers but on two plates.

PARKINSON (For use with 40/1 worm dividing head.)

Side 1.	24, 25, 28, 30, 34, 37, 38, 39, 41, 42, 43
Side 2.	46, 47, 49, 51, 53, 54, 57, 58, 59, 62, 66

(Double-sided plate)

LORCH, LARGE PLATE
          360, 228, 156, 138, 124, 116, 102, 96, 74, 54, 24,
          400, 300, 168, 130, 125, 110, 95, 85, 70, 60, 50, 10

BOLEY & LEINEN TYPE WW
          90, 84, 80, 72, 70, 68, 64, 60, 54, 50
This is a very small plate, and suitable only for use on the sliderest of watchmakers' lathes.

SENIOR (For use with 40/1 worm dividing head)

No. 1	15, 16, 17, 18, 19, 20, 21
No. 2	23, 27, 33, 39, 45, 52

Appendix IV
DIVIDING WITH 60/1 RATIO WORM – MYFORD STANDARD PLATES
MYFORD DIVIDING HEAD OR SUPER-7 BULL-WHEEL

No.	Plate	Turns	Holes	No.	Plate	turns	Holes	No.	Plate	turns	Holes
1	ANY	60	0	34	34	1	26	67	N.A.		
2	ANY	30	0	35	49	1	35	68	34	0	30
3	ANY	30	0	36	45	1	30	69	46	0	34
4	ANY	15	0	37	37	1	23	70	49	0	42
5	ANY	12	0	38	38	1	22	71	N.A.		
6	ANY	10	0	39	91	1	49	72	42	0	35
7	49	8	28	40	32	1	16	73	N.A.		
8	32	7	16	41	41	1	19	74	37	0	30
9	45	6	30	42	49	1	21	75	45	0	36
10	ANY	6	0	43	43	1	17	76	38	0	30
11	77	5	35	44	77	1	28	77	77	0	60
12	ANY	5	0	45	45	1	15	78	91	0	70
13	91	4	56	46	46	1	14	79	N.A.		
14	49	4	14	47	47	1	13	80	32	0	24
15	ANY	4	0	48	32	1	8	81	N.A.		
16	32	3	24	49	49	1	11	82	41	0	30
17	34	3	18	50	45	1	9	83	N.A.		
18	45	3	15	51	34	1	6	84	49	0	35
19	38	3	6	52	91	1	14	85	34	0	24
20	ANY	3	0	53	N.A.			86	43	0	34
21	49	2	42	54	45	1	5	87	29	0	20
22	77	2	56	55	77	1	7	88	N.A.		
23	46	2	28	56	42	1	3	89	N.A.		
24	32	2	16	57	38	1	2	90	45	0	30
25	45	2	18	58	29	1	1	91	91	0	60
26	91	2	28	59	N.A.			92	46	0	30
27	45	2	10	60	ANY	1	0	93	31	0	20
28	42	2	6	61	N.A.			94	47	0	30
29	29	2	2	62	31	0	30	95	38	0	24
30	ANY	2	0	63	42	0	40	96	32	0	20
31	31	1	29	64	32	0	30	97	N.A.		
32	32	1	28	65	91	0	84	98	49	0	30
33	77	1	63	66	77	0	70	99	N.A.		
								100	45	0	27
								360	42	0	7

Numbers marked "N.A." can be divided by using one of two accessory plates available from Myfords.

DIVIDING WITH 65/1 RATIO WORM (ML7 Etc)

The table is worked out for use with the CHRONOS division plate No. DD.61, with additional numbers (marked*) using the DD.63 plate. Above 60 divisions only those available are shown. Numbers Marked † can be divided using DD.66

No.	Plate	Turns	Holes	No.	Plate	Turns	Holes	No.	Plate	Turns	Holes
2	84	32	42	31*	62	2	6	62	62	1	3
3	84	21	56	32	64	2	2	63*	63	1	2
4	84	16	21	33†	132	1	128	64	64	1	1
5	ANY	13	0	34*	34	1	30	65	ANY	1	0
6	84	10	70	35	84	1	72	70	84	0	78
7	84	9	24	36	72	1	58	72	72	0	65
8	72	8	9	37†	74	1	56	75	60	0	52
9	72	7	16	38†	114	1	81	78	78	0	65
10	84	6	42	39	84	1	56	80	80	0	65
11*	88	5	80	40	72	1	45	85*	34	0	26
12	84	5	35	41*	41	1	24	88*	88	0	65
13	ANY	5	0	42	84	1	46	90	72	0	52
14	84	4	54	43	N.A.			91	84	0	60
15	84	4	28	44*	88	1	42	95†	114	0	78
16	64	4	4	45	72	1	32	96	96	0	65
17*	34	3	28	46	N.A.			100	60	0	39
18	72	3	44	47	N.A.						
19	N.A.			48	96	1	34				
20	84	3	21	49*	49	1	16				
21	84	3	8	50	60	1	18				
22*	88	2	84	51	N.A.			120	72	0	39
23	N.A.			52	84	1	21	125	50	0	26
24	72	2	51	53	N.A.			150	60	0	26
25	60	2	36	54*	54	1	11	360	72	0	13
26	84	2	42	55*	88	1	16				
27*	54	2	22	56*	56	1	9				
28	84	2	27	57	N.A.						
29	N.A.			58	N.A.						
30	84	2	14	59	59	1	6				
				60	60	1	5				

The following are given for convenience. Many other large numbers can be divided.

DD61 plate carries rows of 59, 60, 62, 64, 72, 78, 80, 84, 96, 100 holes.
DD63 plate carries rows of 34, 41, 49, 54, 56, 59, 63, 70, 75, 88 holes.

INDEX

A

Addendum	100
Adjustable angleplates	35
Amolco attachment	49
Angle-cutter	15
Angleplates	35
Attachments	42
Autolock chuck	30

B

Backlash	100
Ball-ended slot drills	19
Barring rack, flywheel	83
Belting	46
Blunting	24
Bolts	34
Boring head	20
Bull-wheel indexing	56

C

Cam milling	106
Carbon steel	22
Case studies	70
Chaddock, D.	49, 88, 108
Changewheel dividing	55, 65
Chip formation	12, 27
Chronos Designs Limited	55, 100
Circular pitch	101
Clamps	34
Clearance	23 et seq.
Clearance angles	25
Clock gears	99
Collets	29
Column fluting	97
Combined operations	88
Complex milling	88
Concavity, lathe	20
Connecting rods	80
Cotton rope	46
Coupling rods	80
Crosshead guide seat	76
Cut importance	14
Cutting fluid	70
Cutting frames	8, 9
Cutting speed	25, 27
Cutter holding	28
Cutter nomenclature	23
Cutter storage	112
Cutter types	14 et seq.

D

"Daylight"	11, 50
Dedendum	100
Dedlock chuck	31
Depth of cut	27
Diametral pitch	101
Dividing	52
Division plates	53
Dovetail cutter	18
Down-cut milling	12
Drilling instrument	7

E

End bosses, rounding	81
End mill	16, 29
"Engineering" gears	99
Engine frames	88
Engine standard	93
Expansion links	85

F

Facing a cylinder block	78
Feed rate	26
Feeds and speeds	25
Finishing	71
Finishing cuts	26
Fixed slide	37
Fluted teeth	13
Fluting	86, 96
Flycutters	19, 71, 105
Forked end forming	83
Form cutter	14
Form flycutting	21

G

Gang milling	83
Gearcutting	99, 103
Gear tooth cutters	101
Grinding cutters	114

H

Headstock mandrel division	54, 64
Helical fluting	96
Hemingway, N.S.	64
High speed steel	22
Holtzapffel	6
Home-made cutters	111
Hornblocks	76
Horological gears	99

I

Industrial speeds and feeds 118
Indexing 52

J

Jack, toolmaker's 36
Jig for expansion links 85

L

Lagging strips, simulating 85
Lathe 6, 10
Leadscrew dividing 60
Leather belts 46
Locomotive hornblocks 76
Lorch plates 56
Lorch sawtable 84

M

Machine vices 35
Mason, L.C. 56
Master and slave chuck 31
Maudslay, H. 9
Milling arbor 28
Milling attachments 48
Milling cutters 10, 12
Milling spindles 42
Miscellaneous cutters 21
Model Engineering Services Limted 62, 115
Module 101
Mole, A.N. & Company 49
Motorised drive unit 48
Myford dividing head 62
Myford-Rodney attachment 50
Myfords 37

N

Nasmyth, J. 9
Negative rake 23
Nomenclature, cutter 23
Nylon cord belt 46

O

Offhand grinding 116
Ornamental chucks 7
Overhead gear 6, 44

P

Packing 34
Parallels 34
Pinions 103
Pitch circle 100
Pitch comparison 102
Plastic belting 47
Port milling 78
Potts spindle 42
Power limits 11
Pressure angle 100
Procedures 70
Profiling 16, 49, 73, 109
Protractor dividing 59

Q

Quorn grinder 27, 87, 112

R

Radford, J. 57
Rake 23 et seq.
Rake angles 25
Rate of feed 25
Rawhide mallet 35
Reference planes 33
Relieved teeth 13
Rippa cutter 17
Rose engine 6
Rotary table 54
Rounding end bosses 81

S

Sawing 83
Saw table 84
Sector arms 67
Sharpening 113
Shell end-mill 17
Shock load 12, 28
Side and face cutter 14
Slabbing cutter 14
Slab cutting 73
Slide valve, making 79
Slitting saws 14, 74
Slot drill 18
Slotting 74
Slotting cutter 14
Solids of revolution 6
Special cutters 21
Speeds and feeds 25
Spindle drives 45
Spindles 42
Spring back 12
Swivelling slide 37

T

Tap fluting	86
Taper rods	81
Tee-bars	34
Tee slot bar	75
Tee slot cutter	18
Tempering	112
Thomas, G.H.	57, 61, 63
Thread milling	95
Throwaway cutters	19
Tooth form	13
Tooth load	26

V

Vee blocks	36
Vertical engine standard	93
Vertical slide	37
Vices	35

W

Westbury vertical slide	38, 61
Wheel cutting engines	7
Wild, J.M.	48, 100
Woking Precision Models	38, 61
Wood blocks	39
Wood pulleys	46
Woodruffe keyway cutter	18
Worm dividing	53